Haynes
THE BOOK ®

A Guide to Automotive Air Conditioning Systems

Steve Rendle

(3740 - 160)

© **Haynes Publishing 2000**

A book in the **Haynes Service and Repair Manual Series**

ISBN **1 85960 740 3**

British Library Cataloguing in Publication Data
A catalogue record for this book is available from the British Library.

ABCDE
FGHIJ
KLMNO
PQRST

Printed in the USA

Haynes Publishing
Sparkford Nr Yeovil, Somerset BA22 7JJ, England

Haynes North America, Inc.
861 Lawrence Drive, Newbury Park, California 91320, USA

Editions Haynes
Tour Aurore – IBC, 18 Place des Reflets,
92975 Paris La Defense 2, Cedex, France

Haynes Publishing Nordiska AB
Box 1504, 751 45 UPPSALA, Sverige

Contents

Chapter 1 Basic theory of air conditioning system operation

Introduction   Page   **1•1**

The comfort zone   Page   **1•2**

Heat   Page   **1•3**

Heat transfer   Page   **1•4**

Air conditioning   Page   **1•6**

Chapter 2 Air conditioning system components

Introduction   Page   **2•1**

Basic types of air conditioning system   Page   **2•2**

Air conditioning system main components   Page   **2•4**

Air conditioning system control components   Page   **2•19**

Refrigerants   Page   **2•31**

Compressor oils   Page   **2•33**

Chapter 3 Typical air conditioning systems

Introduction   Page   **3•1**

High and low sides of the air conditioning system   Page   **3•2**

Manually-controlled air conditioning systems   Page   **3•4**

Automatic air conditioning/climate control systems   Page   **3•9**

Chapter 4 Tools and equipment

Introduction   Page   **4•1**

What tools are needed?   Page   **4•2**

Chapter 5 Safety

Introduction   Page   **5•1**

General safety   Page   **5•2**

Air conditioning system safety precautions   Page   **5•3**

Contents

Chapter 6 Service and repair procedures

Introduction	Page	6•1
Air conditioning system do's and don'ts	Page	6•2
Service valves	Page	6•3
Regular servicing	Page	6•7
Basic service procedures	Page	6•8
Basic repair procedures	Page	6•30

Chapter 7 Fault diagnosis

Introduction	Page	7•1
Fault diagnosis sequence	Page	7•3
Fault diagnosis flow charts	Page	7•4
General fault diagnosis procedures	Page	7•11
Manifold gauge tests	Page	7•14

Chapter 8 Air conditioning system service specifications

Introduction	Page	8•1
Refrigerant temperature/pressure relationships	Page	8•2
Vehicle manufacturers' refrigerant and compressor oil recommendations	Page	8•3
Compressor manufacturers' compressor PAG oil grade recommendations	Page	8•4
Compressor manufacturers' compressor oil capacity recommendations	Page	8•5

Reference

Conversion factors	Page	REF•1
General repair procedures	Page	REF•2
Glossary of technical terms	Page	REF•3
Tools and working facilities	Page	REF•8

Index

	Page	REF•10

Introduction

There was a time when any competent mechanic understood the basic systems of a vehicle pretty well, but nowadays the automotive 'jack-of-all-trades' is a dying breed! In recent years, vehicle systems have become progressively more complicated, partly because of legislation, and partly because of the availability of new technology. Nowadays, a significant investment in training and tools is necessary in order to fully understand and service all the systems likely to be encountered on a modern well-equipped vehicle. As a result, today we often find mechanics and technicians who specialise in a particular area of expertise, for example transmission specialists, engine management specialists, and of course air conditioning specialists. This has created the aura of a 'black art' around some subjects.

Automotive air conditioning is certainly one subject which seems to be shrouded in mystery to many DIY mechanics, and many professionals as well. This is probably because until recently there was little need to know anything about air conditioning, and also because of the specialist equipment required to carry out any work on the systems and components. Only a professional specialist, or a garage which handles a significant amount of air conditioning work, will be able to justify the necessary investment in equipment.

Most vehicle manufacturers produce information on how to service their specific air conditioning systems, and how to diagnose problems using their own special equipment, but there's little information available to explain the basic principles of operation. A good grasp of basic theory will help to remove the mystery from any air conditioning system.

If carefully read and understood, this book should help the reader to understand the fundamentals of air conditioning systems. It begins with an explanation of basic air conditioning theory, followed by descriptions of several typical systems, and a brief description of each of the main system components. The remainder of the book is devoted to routine maintenance, service procedures, repairs and troubleshooting. Component removal and refitting procedures and compressor overhaul procedures are not included. Component removal and refitting procedures vary considerably from vehicle to vehicle, and even between different models in a vehicle range, and there is insufficient space in this book to include full details. In most cases, compressor overhaul is not an economic proposition; specialist tools are required which may only be suitable for use on certain types of compressor, and once the cost of the time taken for overhaul is considered, it's almost certain to be more economical to fit a reconditioned, or even a new unit.

Little mention is made in this book of heating systems, because heating systems are relatively straightforward to maintain and repair (full details can be found in the appropriate Haynes *Service and Repair Manual*, where applicable). Although heating and air conditioning systems are closely interrelated (on some vehicles both systems may be controlled by an automatic climate control system), this book concentrates purely on air conditioning systems.

Note: *Although this book contains comprehensive information on air conditioning service procedures, repairs and troubleshooting, it is strongly recommended that anyone intending to carry out work on an air conditioning system for the first time attends a recognised automotive air conditioning training course, which includes some practical work. Air conditioning work is not a task for the DIY mechanic – any mistakes made can be costly, both in terms of safety and financially.*

Acknowledgements

We would like to thank all of those people at Sparkford and elsewhere who helped in the production of this manual. Special thanks are due to George Pinder of TVE Air Conditioning Services, Chard; Carey Shakespeare and Jim McClean of Motor Climate Services (UK), Birmingham; and Eric Mitchell of MasterTech. Thanks are also due to Ian Grant of 9F Ltd, and Paul Holmes of Airparts Europe (The Vehicle Air Conditioning Training School, Lincolnshire).

Chapter 1
Basic theory of air conditioning system operation

1

Contents

Introduction . . . . .1•1
The comfort zone . . . . .1•2
Heat . . . . .1•3
Heat transfer . . . . .1•4
   Heat moves from warmer to cooler substances . . . . .1•4
   Convection, conduction and radiation . . . . .1•4

Air conditioning . . . . .1•6
   What is automotive air conditioning? .1•7
   Heat transfer . . . . .1•7
   Latent heat of vaporisation . . . . .1•8
   How does a vehicle air conditioning system work? . . . . .1•9
   Refrigerants . . . . .1•11

Introduction

Before attempting any kind of work on an air conditioning system, it's essential to understand the basic principles of air conditioning operation. If you understand these principles, it will help greatly with maintenance, repair and fault diagnosis work.

This Chapter explains the basic theory of how an air conditioning system works, which will hopefully prove interesting, and will help you to avoid trouble when you tackle the procedures explained in later Chapters.

The comfort zone

Research has shown that most people feel comfortable in a relatively narrow temperature range of about 21 to 27°C (70 to 80°F) **(see illustration)**. When the effect of humidity is taken into consideration, this range becomes a little wider. Humidity is simply a measure of the amount of moisture (water vapour) in the air. When the air has absorbed as much moisture as it can, the relative humidity is said to be 100%. If the humidity is relatively high, say 70%, we may still feel comfortable at temperatures in the teens, and if the humidity is low enough, say 30%, we can even tolerate temperatures in the low-30s without too much discomfort. Humidity varies with temperature, because warm air can absorb more moisture than cold air.

The key to whether we feel hot or cold is the ability of our body perspiration to evaporate quickly and easily. If the air is dry, perspiration evaporates quickly and the heat leaving the body makes it feel cool. When the humidity is high, perspiration cannot evaporate as quickly (the air is already full of moisture), so less body heat is lost, and we feel warmer.

In practical terms, this means that we can feel just as comfortable when the temperature is 27°C and the relative humidity is 30%, as when the temperature is 21°C and the relative humidity is 90%.

Many automotive air conditioning and heating systems are integrated into a 'climate control' system which controls the temperature, humidity and air circulation by cooling the air inside the passenger compartment when it's hot outside, and heating it when the air is cold. In the following Sections, we'll examine the basic principles which enable air conditioning and heating systems to do their jobs.

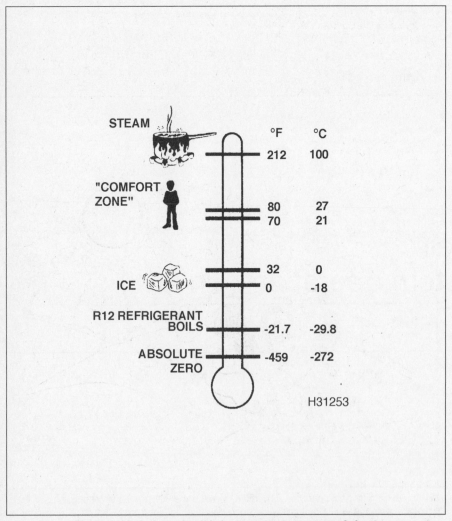

Most people feel comfortable in a temperature range of about 21 to 27°C (70 to 80°F)

Heat

Without 'heat', a heating system would be impossible, and air conditioning would be unnecessary. What exactly is heat? Here's what the dictionary has to say:

Heat 1. *The energy transferred as a result of a difference in temperature.*

The dictionary goes on to give other definitions for heat, but the one above best describes heat for the purposes of this explanation. Heat is basically energy.

Energy takes many forms, reveals its presence in many different ways, and can be transformed from one form to another in many different ways, but heat energy is always present. Let's look at a few examples.

The sun gives off vast amounts of energy of different kinds, heat being one of the more obvious ones **(see illustration)**. On a smaller scale, any fire also gives off heat. The pistons and connecting rods in an internal combustion engine convert the chemical energy released in the combustion of air and fuel into the kinetic energy required to turn the crankshaft, and heat energy. Whenever a driver applies the brakes to stop a vehicle, the friction generated between the brake friction material and the metal discs and/or drums transforms the kinetic energy of the moving vehicle into heat.

When most of us hear the word 'heat', we don't tend to think of kinetic energy, friction, fires or the sun. Instead, we tend to think of the *effect* of heat on our bodies when we're close to a heat source. In other words, the word 'heat' tends to make us think of the sensation of being hot. This is because we are quite sensitive to heat, or the absence of it.

Remember that there is a relatively narrow temperature range in which we feel comfortable. Some people have learned to survive at the extreme edges of this range, but the majority of us prefer to be in the comfort zone between about 21 to 27°C (70 to 80°F). Put another way, we need the right amount of heat to feel comfortable. This is why heating, and more recently, air conditioning systems have become so popular in vehicles; without them we inevitably sometimes feel uncomfortable.

1

H31160

The sun gives off vast amounts of energy of different kinds, heat being one of the more obvious ones

Heat transfer

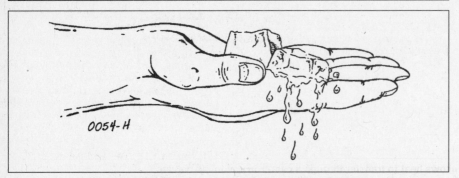

0054-H

Heat always moves from a warmer to a cooler substance

Heat moves from warmer to cooler substances

A basic characteristic of heat is that it always moves from a warmer to a cooler substance. For example, if you place an ice cube in your hands and hold it for a minute, your hands feel cold and the ice cube starts melting **(see illustration)**. This is because the heat is transferring from your hands to the ice cube. Now let's look at the three means by which heat is transferred.

Convection, conduction and radiation

Convection is the movement of heat that occurs in liquids and gases when a heated portion rises and is replaced by a cooler portion, creating a circular movement known as a 'convection current' **(see illustration)**. When air warmer than the surrounding air is forced into the passenger compartment, it moves up, forcing the cooler air down. This constant displacement of cooler air by warmer air eventually distributes the heated air evenly throughout the passenger compartment.

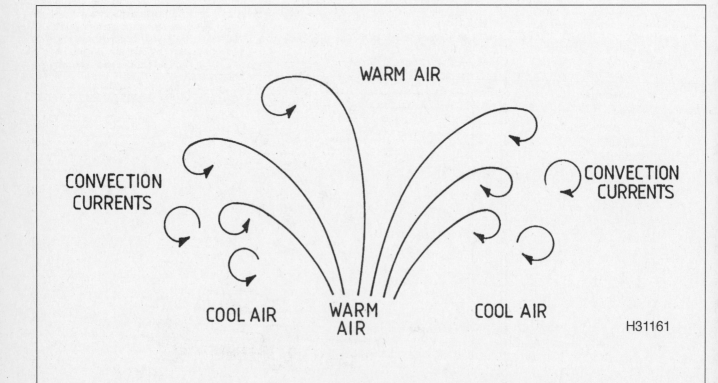

WARM AIR

CONVECTION CURRENTS

CONVECTION CURRENTS

COOL AIR

WARM AIR

COOL AIR

H31161

Warm air rises, which forces cooler air down, creating convection currents

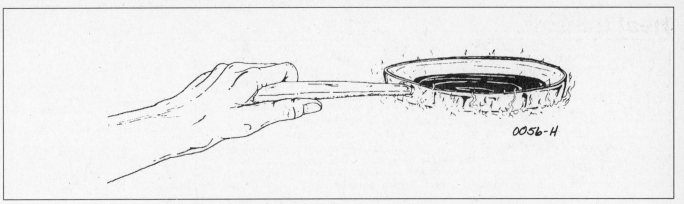

Conduction allows heat to transfer through a cast-iron pan to the handle

Conduction is the transfer of heat through a solid material. If you pick up a cast-iron pan from a cooker, you'll normally find that the handle is warm **(see illustration)**. The heat has been conducted through the hot metal pan to the cooler handle. If you do exactly the same with an aluminium pan, you may find that the handle is too hot to hold. This is because the rate of heat transfer depends on the thermal conductivity of the material, and aluminium is a better thermal conductor than cast-iron. Most heat exchangers (devices which transfer heat from one substance, usually a liquid, to another, usually air) are made from materials such as aluminium or copper, which are amongst the best thermal conductors.

Radiation is the transfer of heat by waves located in the infra-red portion of the electromagnetic spectrum. Because infra-red waves have wavelengths longer than those of visible light waves, they are invisible. When you see 'heat waves' rising from a hot road surface, or from the bonnet of your car on a hot day, you're seeing the effect of radiation.

Similarly, when you feel the heat on a sunny day, it's because infra-red waves from the sun are radiating through space and the earth's atmosphere, hitting your body, and warming it up **(see illustration)**. The most important thing to remember about radiation is that anything that's heated will give off radiating heat.

We can use these three methods of heat transfer to describe a vehicle heating system. At the heart of the system is a small heat exchanger, commonly known as the heater matrix. The heater matrix is a convoluted section of metal tubing through which hot engine coolant is pumped. The heat in the coolant moves through the walls of the tubes and into hundreds of tiny, wafer-thin cooling fins attached to the tubing (conduction). An electric fan blows air through the heater matrix, and heat is transferred from the matrix fins to the cooler air as it passes over them (radiation). This heated air is then forced through a series of ducts and outlets into the passenger compartment, where it warms the air (convection).

Radiated heat from the sun warms a car on a sunny day

1

Air conditioning

When a vehicle is exposed to direct sunlight whilst parked, or whilst being driven on a hot day with the windows wound up, temperatures inside can become uncomfortable. Heat radiated by the sun falls on the metal and glass surfaces of the roof, body panels and windows, is conducted through the vehicle's body, and is radiated into the passenger compartment. Heat radiating from the hot road surface enters the vehicle in a similar way. The engine, exhaust system and transmission all radiate a large amount of heat which finds its way into the passenger compartment. Even the occupants themselves give off heat, and all this can add up to make the inside of the vehicle feel very uncomfortable **(see illustration)**.

If an air conditioning system is fitted, it can remove this uncomfortable heat from the vehicle interior, and make things much more comfortable. An air conditioning system is really a system which removes heat, rather than a system which cools. A typical air conditioning system is capable of maintaining the air inside a vehicle at a temperature 10 to 15ºC (50 to 59ºF) cooler than the ambient air temperature outside the vehicle. Bear in mind that no air conditioning system is capable of producing very cold temperatures inside a vehicle on a very hot day, but a temperature inside the vehicle of 15ºC below the ambient temperature should always feel relatively comfortable to the occupants.

Although you may be able to service an air conditioning system without really understanding how it works, you'll have difficulty troubleshooting if things go wrong. Taking the time to read and understand the following explanations will help you to understand the servicing and maintenance procedures, and should help with fault diagnosis if you have problems.

On a hot day, the inside of a vehicle can feel very uncomfortable

An air conditioning system removes heat from the passenger compartment

What is automotive air conditioning?

Air conditioning is the process by which air is cooled, cleaned and dehumidified before entering or re-entering the passenger compartment. Basically, an air conditioning system removes heat from the passenger compartment by absorbing it and carrying it outside, where it's released into the atmosphere **(see illustration)**.

This process is possible because we've learned how to manipulate three simple natural phenomena:
1) *Heat transfer.*
2) *The latent heat of vaporisation.*
3) *The effect of pressure on boiling or condensation.*

It's not possible to fully understand air conditioning until you understand these three underlying principles, because they form the basis of all air conditioning systems.

Heat transfer

As we've already discussed, if two materials at different temperatures are placed near each other, the heat from the warmer material will always travel to the colder material until both are at the same temperature.

Take for example a bottle of warm beer sitting next to a tray full of ice cubes on a table. The colder tray of ice cubes does not transfer its colder temperature to the bottle of beer next to it. Instead, the heat in the beer flows to the ice cubes **(see illustration)**.

How much heat? In order to express the amount of heat that transfers from one substance to another, various standard units of measurement have been created. For the sake of argument, we'll use kilojoules as our unit of measurement during our discussion. Remember that heat is a form of energy, so a kilojoule is a measurement of heat energy.

Heat will flow from a warm bottle of beer to a tray of ice cubes, causing them to melt

1

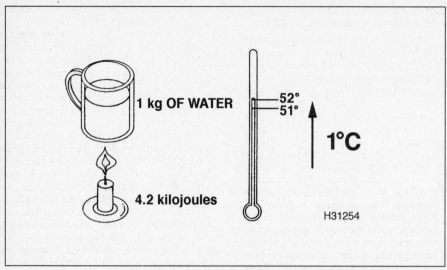

4.2 kilojoules of heat is required to raise the temperature of 1 kg of water by 1°C

It takes approximately 4.2 kilojoules of heat to raise the temperature of 1 kg of water by 1°C. Therefore, to raise the temperature of 1 kg of water (not ice) from 0°C to 100°C, 4.2 kilojoules of heat must be added for each °C rise in temperature, or a total of approximately 420 kilojoules **(see illustration)**. Conversely, in order to lower the temperature of 1 kg of water from 100°C to 0°C, 420 kilojoules of heat must be removed from the water.

Latent heat of vaporisation

And now for a piece of nature's magic! When a liquid boils (changes to a gas), it absorbs heat without raising the temperature of the resulting gas. When the gas condenses (changes back to a liquid), it gives off heat without lowering the temperature of the resulting liquid.

Referring back to the previous example of heat transfer, if 1 kg of water at a temperature of 0°C is placed in a container over a flame, with each 4.2 kilojoules of heat that the water absorbs from the flame, the temperature of the water rises by 1°C. So, after it has absorbed 420 kilojoules of heat, the water reaches a temperature of 100°C. Now, a strange thing happens. Even though the flame continues to transfer heat to the water, the temperature of the water remains at 100°C.

The water also starts to boil, changing from a liquid to a gaseous state, and the boiling continues until the entire kilogram of water has passed into the atmosphere as a vapour. If, instead of escaping into the atmosphere, the vapour from the whole kilogram of water were somehow trapped in a container and checked with a thermometer, it too would indicate a temperature of 100°C. In other words, even though the flame undoubtedly transferred more than 420 kilojoules of heat to the water, there could have been no more than a 100°C rise in the water's temperature. Where did the rest of the heat go? It was absorbed by the water as it boiled off and disappeared with the vapour. If the vapour contacted cool air, however, the hidden heat would reappear and flow into the cooler air as the vapour condensed back to water. In scientific terms, this phenomenon is known as the latent, or hidden, heat of vaporisation.

Water has a latent heat of vaporisation of approximately 2300 kilojoules per kilogram, and a boiling point of 100°C. What this means is that as 1 kg of water reaches a temperature of 100°C, it will absorb 2300 kilojoules of heat as it changes to vapour. Conversely, the vapour will give off 2300 kilojoules of heat as it condenses back to water **(see illustration)**.

This transfer of heat which occurs when a liquid boils or a vapour condenses, is the basic principle of operation of all air conditioning systems.

The effect of the boiling point

If we place our bottle of beer, for example, at a room temperature of say, 21°C next to a container of boiling water, the heat will flow from the (higher temperature) water to the (cooler temperature) beer. This means that we get warm beer. The boiling water cannot absorb any heat from the beer because the boiling point of water is higher than the temperature of the beer.

A refrigerant is basically a substance used in an air conditioning system to absorb, carry and release heat. When considering liquid refrigerants for use in an air conditioning system, the amount of heat that the liquid can absorb as it vaporises is not the only critical characteristic to consider. The liquid must also have a low boiling point; the temperature at which the liquid boils must be lower than the temperature of the substance to be cooled. The boiling point of the refrigerants used in vehicle air conditioning systems is generally between −25 and −30°C (−13 and −22°F), which is well below the temperature of any vehicle passenger compartment.

The effect of pressure on boiling or condensation

The saturation temperature (the temperature at which boiling or condensation occurs) of a liquid or vapour increases as the pressure to which it is subjected increases.

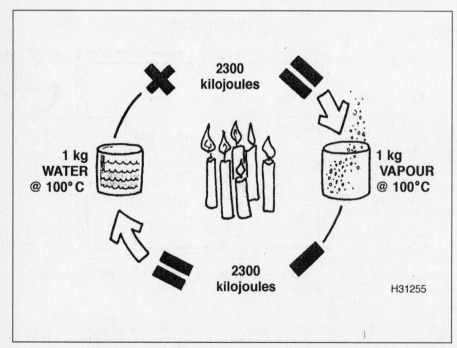

Water has a latent heat of vaporisation of 2300 kilojoules

How does a vehicle air conditioning system work?

Now we've looked at a few of the laws of nature, and seen how these natural phenomena affect liquids and vapours, we can take a look at how these phenomena can be manipulated to provide us with an air conditioning system. We'll discuss the detailed operation of a vehicle air conditioning system later, but we can outline a few of the basics at this stage.

In a typical vehicle air conditioning system, high pressure liquid refrigerant in the condenser is released into the evaporator, via a device which decreases the refrigerant pressure. The decrease in pressure and partial boiling of the refrigerant lowers its temperature to the new boiling point. As the refrigerant flows through the evaporator, the passenger compartment air passes over the outside surfaces of the evaporator fins. The refrigerant boils, absorbing heat from the air, and cooling the air flowing into the passenger compartment. The heat from the passenger compartment is carried away by the refrigerant vapour. The air conditioning cycle is now underway. To complete the cycle, three things need to happen:

1) *The heat in the vapour must be disposed of.*
2) *The vapour must be converted back to liquid for re-use.*
3) *The liquid must be returned to the starting point in the refrigeration cycle.*

The compressor and condenser perform these functions. The compressor pumps the refrigerant vapour – which contains the latent or hidden heat – out of the evaporator, then forces it, under high pressure, into the condenser, which is usually located in front of the radiator at the front of the vehicle. The increased pressure in the condenser raises the refrigerant temperature to a point higher than the outside air. As the heat transfers from the hot vapour to the cooler air, the refrigerant condenses back to a liquid. The liquid, now under high pressure, returns through the system ready for re-use **(see illustration).**

So, how can heat be transferred from a comparatively cooler vehicle passenger compartment to the hot outside air? The answer lies in the difference between the refrigerant pressure that exists in the evaporator, and the pressure in the condenser. In the evaporator, the suction of the compressor reduces the pressure and the boiling point below the temperature of the passenger compartment, so heat transfers from the (warmer) passenger compartment to the (cooler) boiling refrigerant. In the condenser, which is pressurised by the compressor, the condensation point is raised above the temperature of the outside air, so heat transfers from the (warmer) condensing refrigerant to the (cooler) outside air.

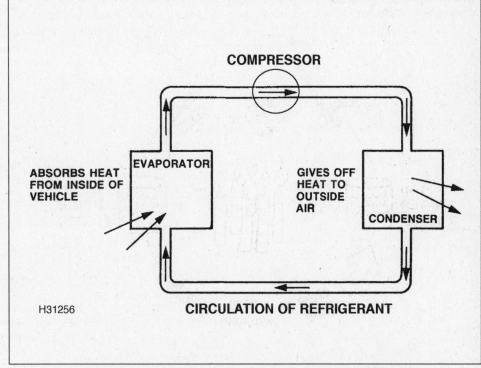

H31256

In the simplest form, refrigerant absorbs heat from the passenger compartment at the evaporator, and transfers the heat to the outside air at the condenser

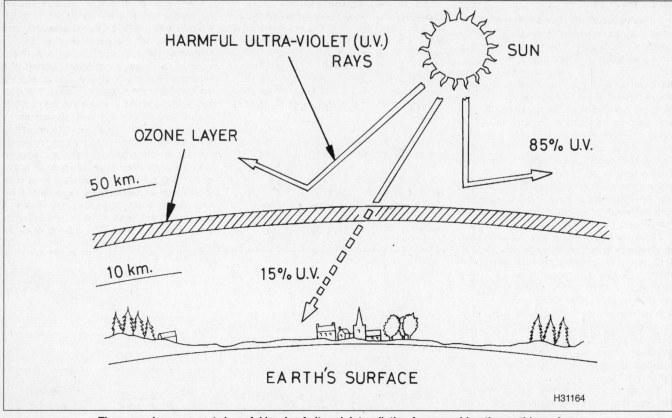

The ozone layer prevents harmful levels of ultra-violet radiation from reaching the earth's surface

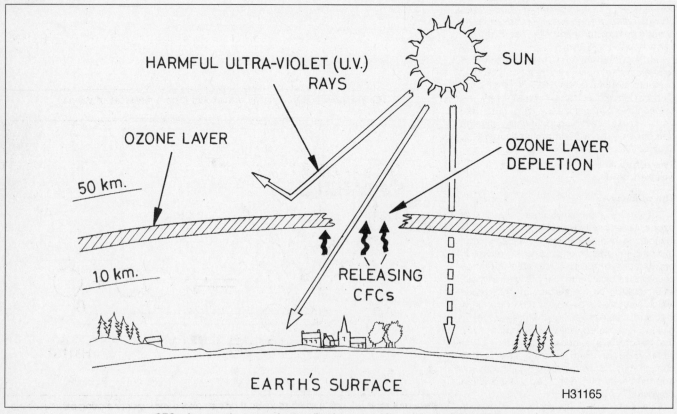

CFCs damage the ozone layer, allowing more ultra-violet radiation through

Refrigerants

As we've already discovered, the refrigerant used in a vehicle air conditioning system must have a low boiling point, and a high latent heat of vaporisation. Another important characteristic to consider is the relationship between temperature and pressure; if the pressure of the refrigerant is low, the temperature should also be low. Refer to the refrigerant temperature/pressure charts in Chapter 8 for details of refrigerant temperature/pressure relationships.

For an air conditioning system to operate at peak efficiency, the refrigerant must reach the coldest state (the lowest pressure) at which it can operate without icing in the evaporator, and its warmest (highest pressure) in the condenser.

There are two refrigerants commonly used in vehicle air conditioning systems, known as R12, and R134a. Other types of refrigerant may be used if the system is serviced, but R12 and R134a are currently the only refrigerants which have been approved by the vehicle manufacturers for use in their air conditioning systems. These refrigerants have been chosen because they are non-toxic in small amounts (as long as they are not exposed to a naked flame), non-corrosive and odourless.

There is one serious problem with refrigerants, and that's their impact on the environment. R12 is a CFC (ChloroFluoro Carbon) chemical, which destroys the earth's ozone layer. For this reason, R12 has been phased out, and is no longer produced in the world's developed countries (production has been banned in EU countries since 1995). R134a has replaced R12 as the approved refrigerant for modern vehicle air conditioning systems. R134a is an HFC (HydroFluoro Carbon) chemical. Note that although the systems work in exactly the same way, R12 and R134a air conditioning system components are NOT interchangeable (see Chapter 2 for more details).

The effect of refrigerants on the environment

The ozone layer

The earth's upper atmosphere contains an ozone layer, which protects the earth's inhabitants (humans, animals and plants) from the harmful effects of ultra-violet radiation produced by the sun. Ultra-violet radiation causes skin cancers in humans and animals, kills plankton on the surface of the oceans which serves as a source of food for marine life, and can destroy agricultural crops by giving them the equivalent of sunburn. Note that the ozone layer doesn't stop all the ultra-violet radiation from reaching the earth's surface, but it does reduce it significantly (by approximately 85%) **(see illustration opposite)**.

So what is ozone? The ozone layer exists in a band between approximately 10 km and 50 km above the earth's surface. In 1985, scientists discovered a hole in the ozone layer at the South Pole. This hole is increasing in size, and now exposes populated areas in parts of South America to the effects of ultra-violet radiation. It has been found that there is a significantly higher-than-average number of cases of skin cancers and cataracts amongst the population in this area **(see illustration opposite)**.

Ozone is a chemical molecule formed from three oxygen atoms. The oxygen molecules which we breathe are formed from two oxygen atoms; for a third atom to join one of these molecules, energy from the sun is needed. The sun provides a particular form of energy which enables an extra oxygen atom to stick to an oxygen molecule to form a molecule of ozone **(see illustration)**. From this, we can see that ozone is only formed when the sun is shining. The Antarctic region around the South Pole has two seasons; a six month summer, when the sun shines constantly, and a six month winter when there is no sun. Because of this, during the Antarctic summer, plenty of ozone is produced, and the hole in the ozone layer gets filled in, but over the winter, when no ozone is produced for six months, the hole appears.

When ultra-violet radiation hits an ozone molecule, one of the oxygen atoms splits off the ozone molecule to from an oxygen molecule and a free oxygen atom. Most of the ultra-violet radiation is absorbed in this process **(see illustration)**. The sun then provides the energy for the oxygen molecule and the extra oxygen atom to joint together again to form ozone, and the cycle is repeated.

The sun provides the energy required to form a molecule of ozone

Ultra-violet radiation is absorbed when it hits an ozone molecule, splitting off one of the oxygen atoms

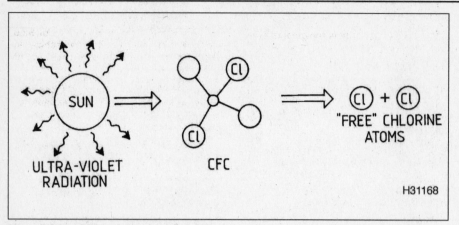

Ultra-violet radiation splits apart R12 CFC molecules to produce 'free' chlorine atoms . . .

. . . which attack the ozone, depleting the ozone layer

The effect of CFCs on the ozone layer

If CFC refrigerant (R12) leaks from an air conditioning system, it will 'fall' to the ground because it's heavier than air. It can take this CFC several years to find its way into the upper atmosphere as it's carried up through the air by dirt, dust and debris. This is why we can't measure the effect of reducing the levels of CFCs yet; it will take a few years for the effects to become visible.

When a CFC reaches the upper atmosphere, it's split apart by ultra-violet radiation, in exactly the same way as described previously for ozone. A molecule of R12 is made up of one carbon, two chlorine and two fluorine atoms (the chemical symbol for R12 is CCl_2F_2). When ultra-violet radiation hits the R12 molecule, it splits off the chlorine atoms, which are then 'free'. The chlorine then attacks the ozone in the atmosphere and depletes it **(see illustrations)**. Scientists estimate that one free chlorine atom can destroy up to ten thousand molecules of ozone, and CFCs have a life span of up to 100 years in the atmosphere! This is why we no longer use R12.

R134a refrigerant is 'ozone-friendly', and has no effect on the ozone layer.

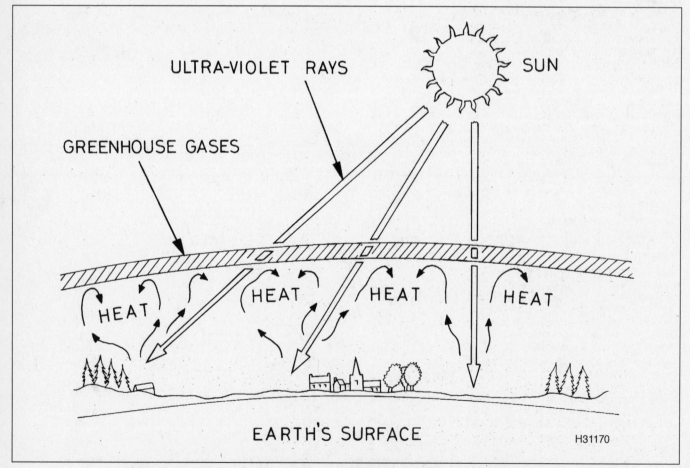

Heat energy cannot escape through the greenhouse gases which causes global warming

The greenhouse effect and global warming

Ultra-violet radiation can pass through clouds, glass and perspex unaffected, but when it hits an object, the radiation changes from ultra-violet to heat radiation, which cannot escape back through the clouds, glass or perspex. This is why it's warm inside a greenhouse on a cool day.

Within the earth's atmosphere, there are various layers of 'greenhouse gases', which have the same effect as the glass or perspex in a greenhouse. Ultra-violet radiation passes through the gases, and hits an object on the earth's surface, or the earth's surface itself, transforming it into heat energy. The heat energy cannot then escape back through the gases, and so it warms the earth, creating global warming **(see illustration opposite)**. Any increase in greenhouse gases will cause an increase in global warming. If there were no greenhouse gases at all, the earth would actually be too cold for us to survive, so we need some global warming, but not too much.

The effect of refrigerants on global warming

To give an idea of how refrigerants affect global warming, we can compare them with the effect of carbon dioxide gas, which is considered to be the single most prominent greenhouse gas (carbon dioxide is produced by most industrial processes, car exhausts, and by burning vegetation). R12 refrigerant has an effect approximately 8500 times greater than carbon dioxide, and R134a refrigerant has an effect approximately 1300 times greater than carbon dioxide. This means that refrigerants add significantly to the problem of global warming.

Protecting the environment

As already mentioned, R12 refrigerant has been phased out, and is no longer produced in the world's developed countries (production has been banned in EU countries since 1995). There are still plenty of cars on the road with air conditioning systems which use R12 refrigerant, but all cars currently in production use R134a.

To reduce the impact on the environment, laws have been passed to make it an offence to release refrigerant into the atmosphere. In the UK, the Environmental Protection Act of 1990 states that:

It is an offence to treat, keep or dispose of a controlled substance in a manner likely to cause pollution to the environment, or harm to human health.

With specific reference to refrigerants, the Act also states that:

It is an offence to deliberately discharge environmentally damaging refrigerant to the atmosphere.

Severe penalties can be imposed on anyone ignoring these laws, including heavy fines and possible imprisonment (up to £20 000 and/or up to 6 months in prison, at the time of writing).

1

Chapter 2
Air conditioning system components

Contents

Introduction . . . . .2•1
Basic types of air conditioning system . . . . .2•2
   Air conditioning system using an expansion valve . . . . .2•2
   Air conditioning system using an orifice tube . . . . .2•3
Air conditioning system main components . . . . .2•4
   Compressor . . . . .2•4
   Condenser . . . . .2•12
   Condenser fan . . . . .2•13
   Evaporator . . . . .2•13
   Blower fan and motor . . . . .2•13
   Filter/drier (expansion valve type systems) . . . . .2•14
   Accumulator (orifice tube type systems) . . . . .2•15
   Expansion valve . . . . .2•16

Orifice tube . . . . .2•18
Air conditioning system control components . . . . .2•19
   Compressor controls . . . . .2•19
   Condenser fan controls . . . . .2•26
   Evaporator controls . . . . .2•26
   Driveability controls . . . . .2•29
   High pressure relief valve . . . . .2•30
Refrigerants . . . . .2•31
   R12 . . . . .2•32
   R134a . . . . .2•32
   Alternative refrigerants . . . . .2•32
Compressor oils . . . . .2•33

2

Introduction

There are five basic components which are used in every automotive air conditioning system (in addition to the connecting pipes and hoses):

  1) Compressor.
  2) Condenser.
  *3) Filter/drier **or** accumulator.*
  *4) Expansion valve **or** orifice tube.*
  5) Evaporator.

No air conditioning system, whether it uses R12 or R134a refrigerant, can operate without all five components. On systems using R134a, the compressor, condenser and the evaporator are physically larger than their counterparts on systems using R12, but the components function in exactly the same way. A number of other components are used to control the system, and to optimise the efficiency of the system, but these components will be discussed in more detail later in this Chapter.

Basic types of air conditioning system

There are two basic types of vehicle air conditioning system. As we discussed in Chapter 1 (*How does a vehicle air conditioning system work?*), in a typical vehicle air condit-ioning system, high pressure liquid refrigerant in the condenser is released into the evap-orator, via a device which decreases the refrigerant pressure. The type of device used to decrease the refrigerant pressure gives us the basic difference between the two types of air conditioning system; the device used may be either an *expansion valve*, or an *orifice tube*.

Let's take a look at the two types of system in more detail.

Air conditioning system using an expansion valve

The five basic components used in this type of system are:

1) *Compressor (driven by the engine)*
2) *Condenser (located at the front of the car, in front of the radiator)*
3) *Filter/drier (located in the engine compartment)*
4) *Expansion valve (usually attached to the evaporator)*
5) *Evaporator (located inside the car, with the heater components behind the facia)*

If we follow the refrigerant flow round the system, starting at the compressor, the **compressor** compresses the refrigerant from a low pressure vapour to a high pressure vapour **(see illustration)**. The high pressure vapour is then passed to the **condenser**, where it is condensed by the cooling air flow to a high pressure liquid. The high pressure liquid is passed to **filter/drier**, where it is cleaned and all moisture is removed. The clean, dry high pressure liquid is passed to the **expansion valve**, where it is changed to a low pressure mixture of liquid and vapour. The low pressure refrigerant mixture is then passed to the **evaporator**, where the remaining liquid is turned back to a low pressure vapour, cooling the air passing over the evaporator as it does so. From the evaporator, the low pressure vapour passes back to the compressor, which pumps it round the system again.

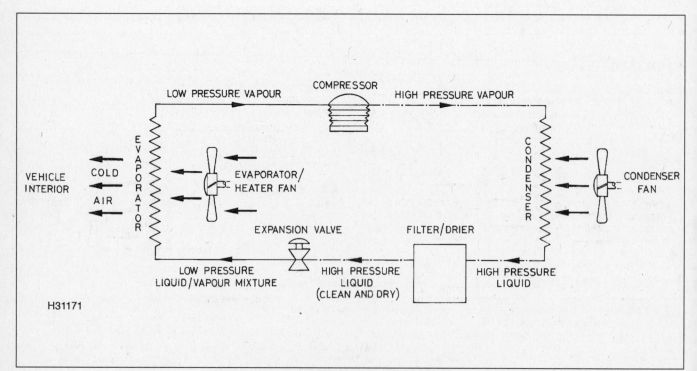

H31171

Basic air conditioning system using an expansion valve

Air conditioning system using an orifice tube

The five basic components used in this type of system are:

1) *Compressor (driven by the engine)*
2) *Condenser (located at the front of the car, in front of the radiator)*
3) *Orifice tube (located in the refrigerant line or in the evaporator)*
4) *Evaporator (attached to the evaporator)*
5) *Accumulator (located in the engine compartment)*

If we follow the refrigerant flow round the system, starting at the compressor, the **compressor** compresses the refrigerant from a low pressure vapour to a high pressure vapour (**see illustration**). The high pressure vapour is then passed to the **condenser**, where it is condensed by the cooling air flow to a high pressure liquid. The high pressure liquid is passed to the **orifice tube**, where the flow is restricted, changing the refrigerant to a low pressure liquid. The low pressure liquid is passed to the **evaporator**, where the liquid is turned partially to a vapour, cooling the air passing over the evaporator as it does so. From the evaporator, the low pressure mixture of liquid and vapour is passed to the **accumulator**, where the remaining liquid is boiled back to vapour. The pure low pressure vapour passes back to the compressor, which pumps it round the system again.

2

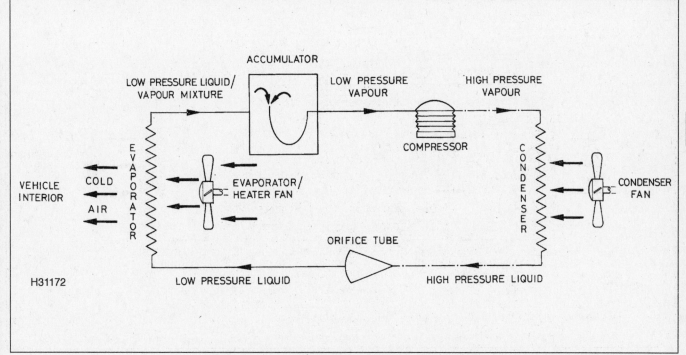

Basic air conditioning system using an orifice tube

Air conditioning system main components

Compressor

Compressors vary in design, but they all perform the same two functions: pumping refrigerant around the system, and increasing the refrigerant pressure and temperature. Note that compressor refrigerant ports are often marked S (suction, ie, low pressure side) and D (discharge, ie, high pressure side).

All compressors are driven by a belt from the engine crankshaft, and it takes an average of 7 to 11 kW (10 to 15 hp) of engine power to drive the compressor.

There are three basic types of compressor; piston type, rotary vane type, and scroll type.

Compressors and liquid refrigerant

Before we discuss how a compressor works, it's necessary to understand that liquid refrigerant cannot be allowed to enter the compressor. One of the laws of nature is that a liquid cannot be compressed. If liquid refrigerant gets into the compressor, it will be unable to do its job, and it will be damaged.

In an 'expansion valve' type air conditioning system, the temperature of the refrigerant vapour leaving the evaporator is high enough to ensure that no liquid is present; any liquid entering the evaporator is changed into vapour before it reaches the evaporator outlet.

In an 'orifice tube' type system, not all the refrigerant is turned into vapour in the evap-orator, so an accumulator is fitted between the evaporator and the com-pressor to boil any liquid back to vapour.

Compressor lubrication

All compressors need some form of lubrication, and this lubrication is provided by oil in the system (the oil is circulated with the refrigerant). Without oil, a compressor will seize, in which case it will have to be renewed, often at great expense. The type of oil used will depend on the type of refrigerant used in the system. Several different grades of oil are available for use in different com-pressors, and the correct oil specified by the compressor manufacturer must always be used to avoid problems. Further details of oils are given in *Compressor oils* later in this Chapter, and in Chapter 6.

Piston-type compressors

Piston compressors have one or more piston(s) arranged either in-line, axially, horizontally-opposed, or in a vee configuration **(see illustration)**.

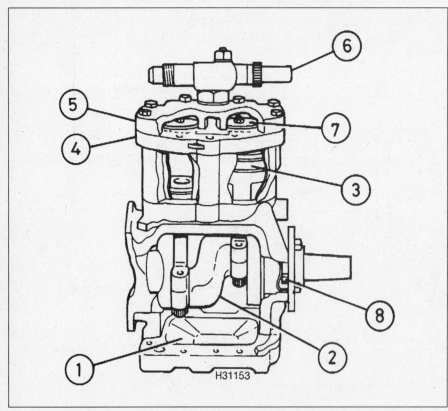

Cutaway view of a typical 2-cylinder piston-type compressor

1 Oil sump	4 Valve plate	7 Reed valve assembly
2 Crankshaft	5 Cylinder head	8 Crankshaft seal assembly
3 Piston and ring assembly	6 Service valve fitting	

Each cylinder of a piston-type compressor goes through an intake stroke, followed by a combined compression/exhaust stroke. Low pressure refrigerant vapour is drawn into the cylinder through an intake reed valve as the piston moves down the cylinder during the intake stroke. As the piston moves back up the cylinder on the compression stroke, the vapour is compressed, increasing both the pressure and temperature of the refrigerant. When a pre-set pressure is reached, the exhaust reed valve opens to allow the refrigerant to move out of the compressor cylinder towards the condenser **(see illustration)**. Effectively, the exhaust reed valve is the start of the high pressure side of the system.

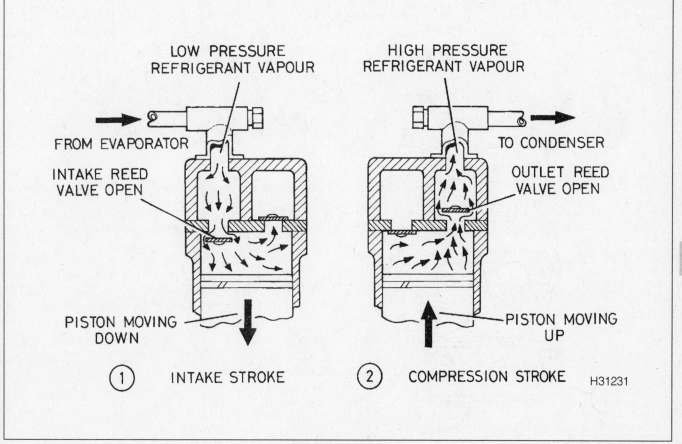

Compressor operation

1 Intake stroke – low pressure refrigerant is drawn into compressor through one-way suction reed valve

2 Compression stroke - refrigerant vapour is compressed into high pressure, high temperature vapour and pushed out through one-way discharge reed valve

The most common piston-type compressors have multiple pistons, operated by a 'squish-plate' (or 'swash-plate') attached to the compressor shaft **(see illustration)**. As the shaft turns, the squish-plate moves the pistons to compress the refrigerant. Many compressors use several sets of twin, horizontally-opposed pistons.

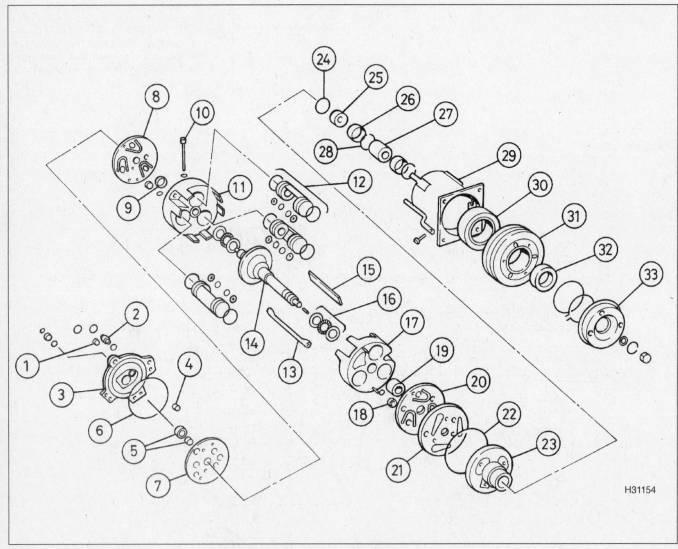

Exploded view of a typical 6-cylinder-type compressor

H31154

1 Low pressure cut-out (superheat) switch	9 Bearing	18 Bush	26 Seal seat
2 Pressure relief valve	10 Oil tube	19 Bearing	27 Sleeve
3 Rear cylinder head	11 Rear cylinder body	20 Front suction reed valve plate	28 Circlip
4 Suction screen	12 Piston assembly	21 Front discharge reed valve plate	29 Casing
5 Oil pump rotors	13 Discharge tube	22 O-ring	30 Clutch coil
6 O-ring	14 Shaft and squish-plate	23 Front cylinder head	31 Pulley
7 Rear discharge valve plate	15 Suction port cover	24 O-ring	32 Bearing
8 Rear suction reed valve plate	16 Thrust bearing and races	25 Seal	33 Clutch plate and hub assembly
	17 Front cylinder body		

Variable-displacement piston-type compressors

Variable displacement piston-type compressors are used on some vehicles **(see illustration)**. Variable displacement compressors run constantly when the air conditioning system is switched on, and the refrigerant flow is controlled by effectively changing the displacement of the compressor to suit the prevailing operating conditions. This type of compressor uses a variable-angle squish-plate to operate the pistons. The angle of the squish-plate is usually controlled via a control valve mounted on the compressor (see *Compressor controls*), which allows varying amounts of high-pressure refrigerant to enter the compressor crankcase. The control valve senses the suction pressure on the low side of the compressor, which varies according to the evaporator temperature and the compressor speed.

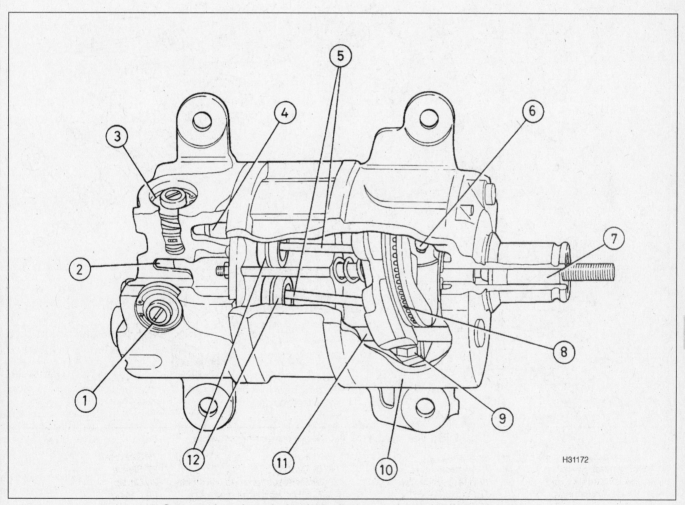

H31172

Cutaway view of a typical variable-displacement piston-type compressor

1 Main control valve	5 Connecting rods	9 Anti-rotation swivel
2 Discharge port	6 Squish-plate drive linkage	10 Crankcase
3 Auxiliary control valve	7 Input shaft	11 Anti-rotation shaft
4 Suction port	8 Thrust bearing squish-plate	12 Pistons

2

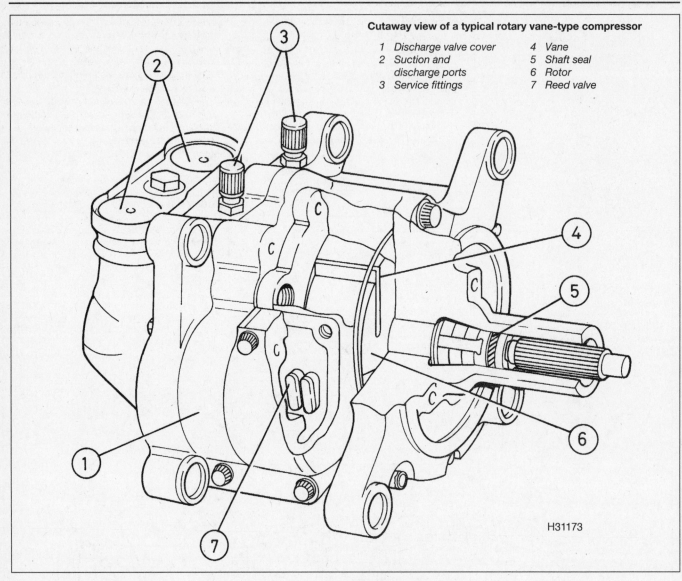

Cutaway view of a typical rotary vane-type compressor

1 Discharge valve cover 4 Vane
2 Suction and 5 Shaft seal
  discharge ports 6 Rotor
3 Service fittings 7 Reed valve

H31173

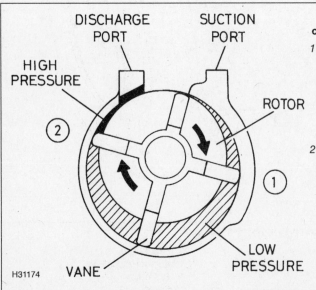

H31174

Rotary vane-type compressor operation

1 *Intake – As a low pressure chamber sweeps by the suction port, low pressure refrigerant vapour is drawn through a one-way reed valve*

2 *Exhaust – As the rotor rotates, the chamber decreases in size, compressing the refrigerant. As the chamber sweeps by the discharge port, high pressure refrigerant is expelled through a one-way reed valve*

Rotary vane-type compressors

Rotary vane-type compressors consist of a rotor with several vanes, and a precisely-shaped housing. As the compressor shaft rotates, the vanes and housing form chambers. The refrigerant is drawn through the intake port into the chambers, which reduce in size as the rotor turns. The outlet port is located at the point where the chambers are at their smallest, where the vapour is completely compressed **(see illustrations)**.

Vane-type compressors have no sealing rings. The vanes are sealed against the housing by centrifugal force and lubricating oil. The lubricating oil sump is located on the outlet side of the compressor, so the high pressure tends to force it around the edges of the vanes into the low pressure side. This action ensures continuous lubrication.

Scroll-type compressors

Scroll-type compressors have two metal scrolls, one fixed and one moveable, which provide an eccentric motion (see illustration). As the compressor shaft rotates, the moveable scroll is driven by an eccentric bushing on the shaft, and refrigerant is forced against the fixed scroll, and towards its centre. The motion creates an increase in pressure towards the centre of the scroll. The refrigerant vapour moves in a circular pattern, and its pressure is increased as it moves towards the centre of the scroll. The high pressure refrigerant is released through a delivery port located at the centre of the scroll (see illustration overleaf).

Scroll-type compressors provide a longer effective compression stroke, and a smoother start-up than other compressor types, and produce less vibration.

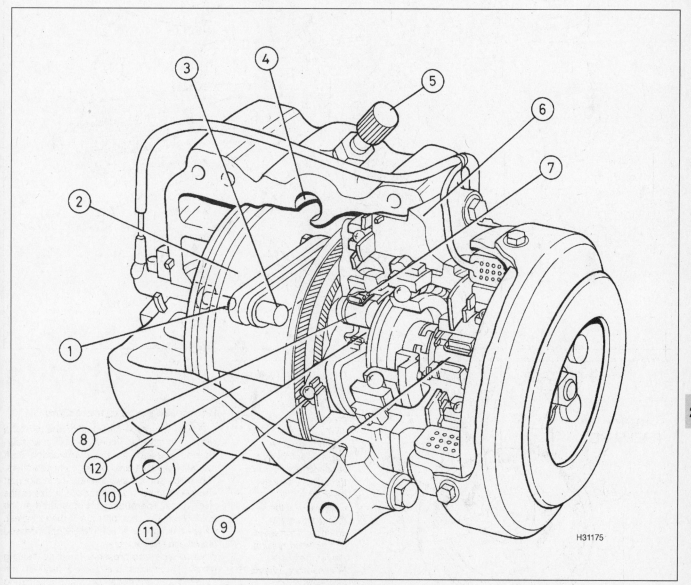

H31175

Cutaway view of a typical scroll-type compressor

1	Refrigerant temperature sensor	5	Low pressure service valve	9	Crankshaft
2	Movable scroll	6	Front plate	10	Eccentric bushing
3	Delivery port	7	Needle bearing	11	Ball coupling
4	Intake port	8	Stud pin	12	Fixed scroll

2

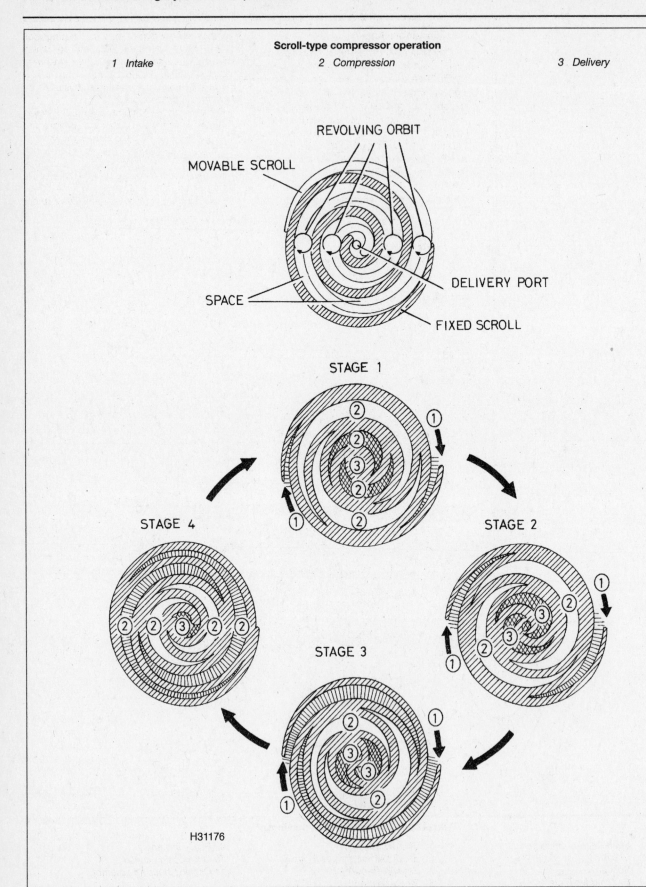

Scroll-type compressor operation

1 Intake   *2 Compression*   *3 Delivery*

REVOLVING ORBIT

MOVABLE SCROLL

DELIVERY PORT

SPACE

FIXED SCROLL

STAGE 1

STAGE 4

STAGE 2

STAGE 3

H31176

Compressor clutch

All vehicle air conditioning compressors are belt-driven from the end of the engine crankshaft. An electro-magnetic clutch disengages the compressor from the drive pulley when compressor operation is unnecessary or is not required. The clutch is operated by the air conditioning control system according to the demands of the air conditioning system. In some systems, the clutch constantly cycles the compressor on and off, whilst in other systems the compressor runs continuously as long as the system is turned on.

Older compressors had a rotating coil clutch design, where the magnetic coil which engages or disengages the compressor was mounted within the pulley, and rotated with the pulley. A stationary coil design is used on all modern compressors.

On the majority of compressors, the coil is mounted behind (or inside) the compressor drive pulley, and the drive plate is mounted at the front of the pulley. When the air conditioning system is switched on, the coil is energised, and the magnetic field created pulls the driveplate into engagement with the pulley, which drives the compressor **(see illustration)**.

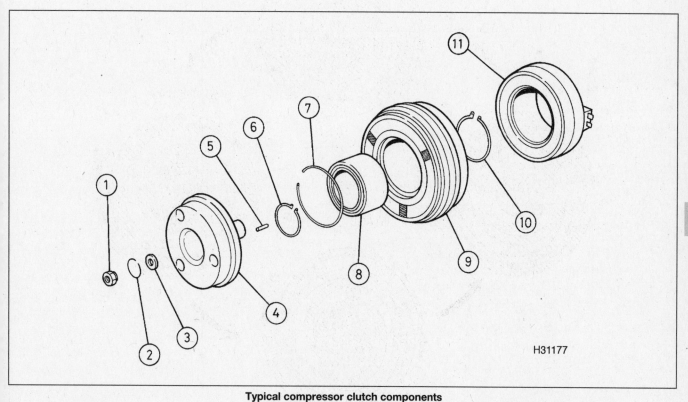

H31177

2

Typical compressor clutch components

1 Shaft nut	5 Clutch hub key	9 Pulley assembly
2 Circlip	6 Bearing-to-compressor circlip	10 Coil housing circlip
3 Spacer	7 Bearing-to-pulley circlip	11 Coil and housing assembly
4 Clutch drive plate	8 Pulley bearing	

Condenser

The condenser is a simple heat exchanger, normally made from copper or aluminium. Several different designs of condensers have been used over the years, including parallel flow, serpentine, and most commonly, tube and fin (similar to a vehicle cooling system radiator). The condenser is usually mounted directly in front of the radiator, so that it can receive the full airflow from the vehicle's forward motion **(see illustration)**.

The condenser receives the heated, pressurised refrigerant vapour from the high pressure side of the compressor. The refrigerant vapour enters at the top of the condenser and flows through the coils, conducting heat through the walls of the tubing and into the cooling fins, then radiating heat from the cooling fins into the atmosphere.

As the refrigerant vapours are cooled and flow down through the condenser, they gradually condense back into liquid form. At the point where the refrigerant vapours condense to liquid, they shed a large amount of latent heat (see Chapter 1).

In an air conditioning system operating under an average heat load, the condenser will have a combination of hot refrigerant vapour in the upper two-thirds, and liquid refrigerant which has condensed in the lower third of the coils. The high pressure liquid refrigerant flows out of the condenser, and moves towards the evaporator.

Bear in mind that an air conditioning condenser is built to withstand the high pressures present in the high side of a system. Never be tempted to fit a cooling system radiator in place of a condenser, as aside from not being designed for air conditioning use, it will probably not cope with the high pressures.

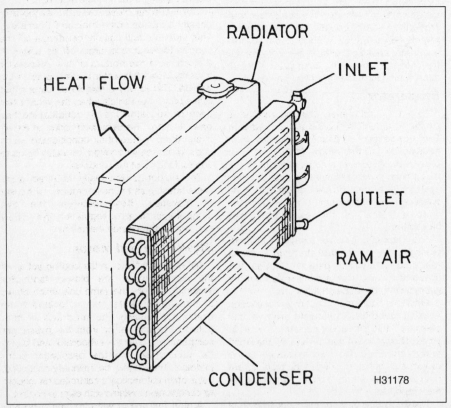

The condenser is usually mounted in front of the radiator to receive the full airflow from the vehicle's forward motion

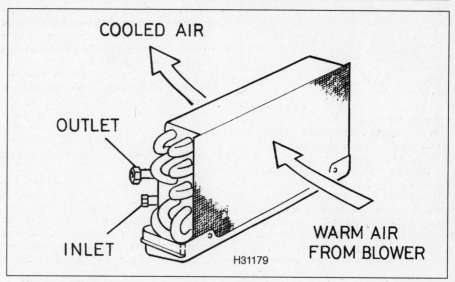

Warm air blown over the evaporator is cooled before passing to the vehicle interior

Condenser fan

The correct operation of the condenser cooling fan is essential to allow the air conditioning system to operate efficiently. The condenser must have an adequate flow of air passing through it at all times to carry heat away from the refrigerant inside.

Most vehicles have an electric condenser cooling fan, but a few vehicles may have a viscous-coupled fan or a fan belt-driven directly from the engine. The condenser may share the radiator cooling fan, but on many vehicles an extra fan is fitted to provide the necessary additional airflow. It is common for the fan to operate whenever the air conditioning system is switched on.

Evaporator

Like the condenser, the evaporator is similar to a vehicle cooling system radiator. The condenser is usually mounted in a housing behind the vehicle facia, so it must provide the maximum amount of heat transfer for a minimum size. When the air conditioning system is turned on, warm air from the passenger compartment is blown through the coils and fins of the evaporator **(see illustration)**.

The evaporator receives refrigerant as a low pressure, low temperature atomised liquid. As the cold refrigerant passes through the evaporator coils, heat is transferred from the warm air into the cooler refrigerant.

When the liquid refrigerant receives enough heat, it vaporises, changing from a low pressure liquid into a low pressure vapour. In an expansion valve type system, all the liquid refrigerant is turned into a vapour in the evaporator, but in an orifice tube type system the refrigerant is only partially vaporised by the evaporator.

The expansion valve or orifice tube controls the amount of refrigerant entering the evaporator to maintain the optimum heat transfer to the refrigerant. If too much refrigerant is allowed to enter, the evaporator floods, which results in poor heat transfer because the higher pressure (and temperature) of the refrigerant prevents it from vaporising easily. If too little refrigerant is allowed into the evaporator, the evaporator is starved, which results in poor heat transfer because the refrigerant vaporises too quickly before passing through the evaporator.

The warm air blown over the evaporator usually contains some moisture (humidity). This moisture will usually condense on the evaporator coils and drain off as water. A drain tube in the bottom of the evaporator housing allows this water to drain outside the vehicle. This is why a puddle of water often forms under the vehicle when the vehicle has been parked after the air conditioning has been running. This dehumidification of the air is an added feature of air conditioning which adds to passenger comfort, and also helps to control fogging of the windows.

The evaporator is usually mounted in the same housing as the heater matrix, with a set of moveable flaps between the two components to allow regulation the airflow and temperature inside the vehicle.

Blower fan and motor

An important factor in the cooling action of the evaporator is the blower fan/motor assembly (usually the same unit which blows air through the heater matrix), located in the evaporator housing. The fan draws air from outside the vehicle, or from the passenger compartment, over the evaporator and blows the cooled air into the passenger compartment. The fan may be manually controlled, but is often automatically controlled on modern air conditioning systems with climate control.

A high fan speed will circulate a greater volume of air, but will not provide maximum cooling. A reduction in fan speed will reduce

2

the volume of air circulated, but the air will remain in contact with the evaporator fins for a longer time. This will allow greater heat transfer from the warm air to the cold refrigerant, and so the coldest air temperature is obtained when the fan is operated at its slowest speed.

Filter/drier (expansion valve type systems)

If moisture is allowed to build up inside an air conditioning system, in some cases the water can react with the refrigerant to form an acidic substance which is highly corrosive to the system components. Moisture can also freeze inside the system and block the refrigerant flow, resulting in no cooling action at the evaporator, and possible damage to the compressor. So, moisture in an air conditioning system can lead to serious problems, and can eventually cause system failure.

A filter/drier (also known as a receiver/drier) is used in expansion valve type air conditioning systems to clean the refrigerant and to remove any moisture. The filter/drier is mounted between the condenser and the evaporator, and consists of a tank, a filter, a drying agent, a pick-up tube and, on some units, a sight glass which allows a view into the refrigerant line **(see illustration)**.

The filter/drier protects the system from moisture. The reservoir contains a drying agent, which may take the form of a bag of desiccant silica gel, although this is being superceded by molecular sieve drying agents on the latest systems. The desiccant can be renewed in some filter/driers, and further details are given in Chapter 6.

The filter/drier also acts as a storage reservoir for liquid refrigerant from the condenser, until it's required by the evaporator (the evaporator requires a varying amount of refrigerant depending on operating conditions).

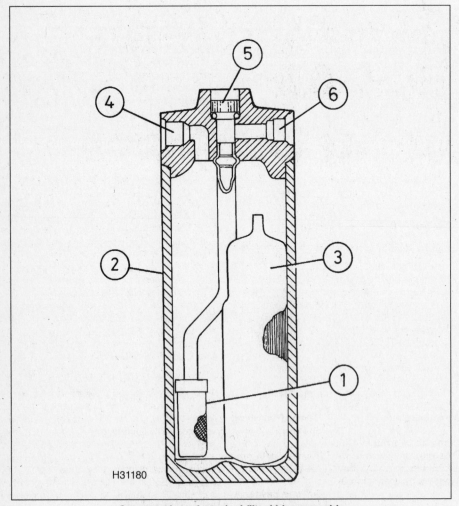

H31180

Cutaway view of a typical filter/drier assembly

1 Filter screen
2 Filter/drier casing
3 Desiccant bag
4 Inlet
5 Sight glass
6 Outlet

Accumulator (orifice tube type systems)

An accumulator is used in orifice tube type air conditioning systems. The accumulator is mounted between the evaporator and the compressor, and consists of a tank, a vapour return tube, and a drying agent **(see illustration)**. The accumulator acts as a storage reservoir for liquid refrigerant passed out of the evaporator (liquid refrigerant will damage the compressor), and boils any remaining liquid refrigerant back to vapour. The liquid will sink to the bottom of the accumulator, whilst the vapour is sucked out through a calibrated vapour tube by the compressor. The accumulator is mounted in the warm engine compartment, and so any liquid refrigerant inside the accumulator rapidly boils to vapour (the boiling point is approximately –30ºC), and is passed to the compressor.

If moisture is allowed to build up inside an air conditioning system, in some cases the water can react with the refrigerant to form an acidic substance which is highly corrosive to the system components. Moisture can also freeze inside the system and block the refrigerant flow, resulting in no cooling action at the evaporator, and possible damage to the compressor. So, moisture in an air conditioning system can lead to serious problems, and can eventually cause system failure.

The accumulator also protects the system from moisture. The reservoir contains a drying agent, which may take the form of a bag of desiccant silica gel, although this is being superceded by molecular sieve drying agents on the latest systems. The desiccant can be renewed in some accumulators, and further details are given in Chapter 6.

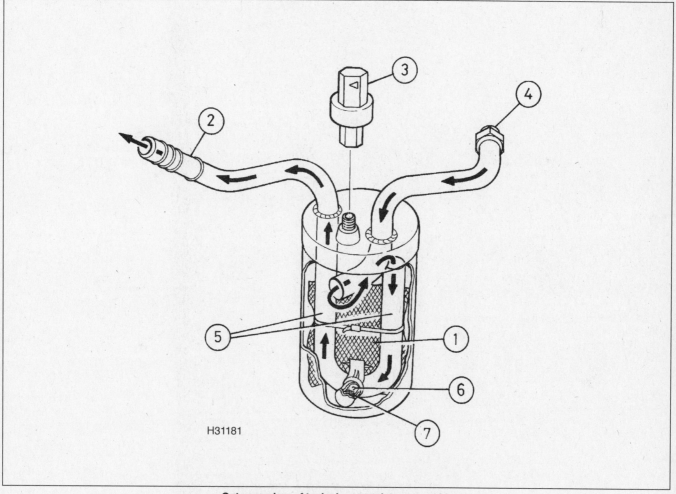

H31181

Cutaway view of typical accumulator assembly

1 Desiccant bag
2 Outlet pipe
3 Pressure-sensitive compressor clutch cycling switch
4 Inlet pipe
5 Vapour return tube
6 Liquid bleed hole
7 Filter screen

Expansion valve

The expansion valve is located between the filter/drier and the evaporator, and its purpose is to control the flow of refrigerant to the evaporator. The expansion valve lowers the pressure (and temperature) of the refrigerant sufficiently to enable the liquid refrigerant to vaporise as it passes through the evaporator coils, absorbing heat from the vehicle interior. The valve assembly consists of a metered orifice, and a thermostatically-controlled valve **(see illustration)**.

A calibrated orifice in the valve lowers the pressure of the incoming refrigerant liquid. Refrigerant from the filter/drier enters the expansion valve as a liquid under high pressure. As the liquid reaches the orifice in the valve, it's forced through the small orifice, and sprayed out the other side. This results in a pressure differential, ie, the liquid enters the orifice at high pressure and temperature, and leaves at a lower pressure and temperature, which allows the atomised mixture of liquid and vapour refrigerant to flow through the evaporator and vaporise completely.

A thermostatically-controlled valve located inside the expansion valve assembly moves from an open to a closed position as required to control the flow of refrigerant passing through the calibrated orifice. This ensures that the evaporator receives the correct quantity of refrigerant to ensure that all the refrigerant entering the evaporator is boiled to a vapour before it leaves. The valve must respond quickly to changes in heat. As increased heat is sensed, the valve will move towards an open position to increase the flow of refrigerant. A decrease in heat will cause the valve to move towards a closed position, restricting the amount of refrigerant entering the evaporator.

Some expansion valves have an inlet filter to prevent any contamination from entering the valve.

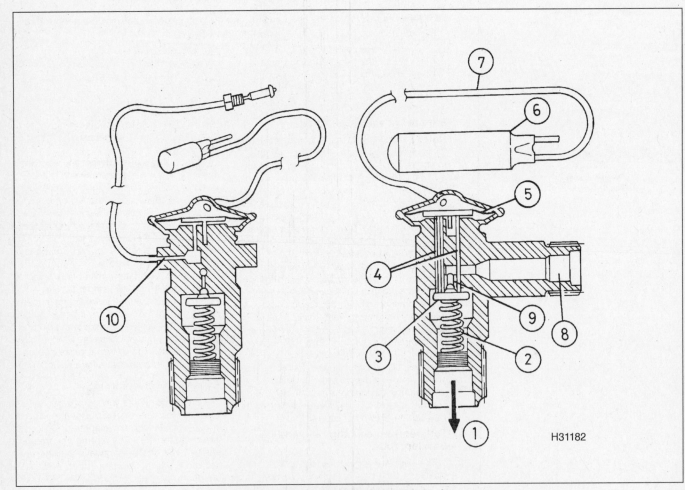

H31182

Cutaway views of a typical expansion valve

1 Refrigerant flow to evaporator inlet	4 Push pins	8 Liquid refrigerant inlet
2 Spring	5 Diaphragm	9 Orifice
3 Valve ball and plate assembly	6 Temperature sensing bulb	10 Pressure equalising passage
	7 Capillary tube	

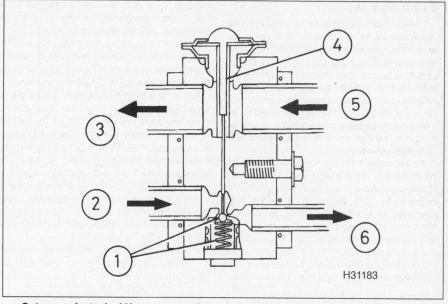

H31183

Cutaway of a typical H-type expansion valve with integral temperature sensor and equalising passage

1 Ball valve and spring
2 Refrigerant flow from condenser
3 Refrigerant flow to compressor
4 Temperature sensor
5 Refrigerant flow from evaporator
6 Refrigerant flow to evaporator

Expansion valve operation

Note: *The following description of expansion valve operation is for a typical design used in many air conditioning systems. Although there may be detailed differences between this and other types, the basic principles are the same for all types of valve.*

In a typical expansion valve, the refrigerant flow is controlled by a spring-loaded valve, which, in turn, is controlled by the difference in pressure above and below a diaphragm. The movement of the diaphragm is transmitted to the valve through operating pins linking the diaphragm plate and the valve.

The pressure above the diaphragm (upper diaphragm chamber) varies according to the pressure inside a temperature sensing bulb (or coil) and capillary tube. The pressure below the diaphragm (lower diaphragm chamber) varies according to the temperature of the refrigerant leaving the expansion valve and entering the evaporator. The valve spring controls a temperature differential across the valve, often known as 'superheat'.

Temperature sensing bulb and capillary tube

The capillary tube, tube end (bulb, coil or plain end) and upper diaphragm chamber form a closed system filled with a temperature-sensitive gas (refrigerant, carbon dioxide or a similar substance).

The capillary tube end is clamped onto the evaporator outlet pipe (or fitted in a housing in the outlet pipe), and is insulated from the outside air using special tape. The capillary

tube end is therefore subjected only to the temperature of the refrigerant as it leaves the evaporator.

Any increase in refrigerant temperature at the evaporator outlet increases the pressure in the capillary tube. This in turn exerts a downward pressure on the expansion valve diaphragm, opening the valve. Similarly, a decrease in refrigerant temperature decreases the pressure in the capillary tube. This reduces the pressure on the diaphragm, allowing the valve to close.

The lower diaphragm chamber is subjected to the pressure of the refrigerant leaving the expansion valve and entering the evaporator. On some types of valve, an internal passage connects the valve refrigerant outlet directly to the lower diaphragm chamber, whilst on other types of valve, an external tube is used to supply refrigerant pressure **(see illustration)**.

Expansion valve spring

A spring below the valve tends to move the valve towards the closed position, and works in conjunction with the diaphragm to control valve movement. The spring is preset to ensure that there is always a differential between the evaporator inlet and outlet temperatures. This temperature differential is often known as 'superheat'. The few extra degrees of heat (typically between 2 and 9°C) ensures that the refrigerant is fully vaporised in the evaporator, and that the vapour leaving the evaporator outlet doesn't contain any droplets of liquid refrigerant when it reaches the compressor.

2

Orifice tube

The orifice tube is located between the condenser and the evaporator, and its purpose is to control the flow of refrigerant to the evaporator. The orifice tube lowers the pressure (and temperature) of the refrigerant sufficiently to enable the liquid refrigerant to vaporise as it passes through the evaporator coils, absorbing heat from the vehicle interior. The orifice tube assembly consists of a tube containing a filter or filters, and a calibrated orifice **(see illustration)**.

The calibrated orifice lowers the pressure of the incoming refrigerant liquid. Refrigerant from the condenser enters orifice tube as a liquid under high pressure. As the liquid reaches the calibrated orifice, it's forced through the small orifice, and sprayed out the other side. This results in a pressure differential, ie, the liquid enters the orifice at high pressure and temperature, and leaves at a lower pressure and temperature, which allows the atomised refrigerant to flow through the evaporator and easily vaporise.

The orifice tube meters a steady flow of refrigerant when the compressor is operating, and so the flow of refrigerant through the orifice tube is controlled by the operation of the compressor. A compressor clutch switch, either a thermostatic type or a pressure-sensitive type is used to switch the compressor on and off. The intermittent operation of the compressor controls the refrigerant flow and pressure.

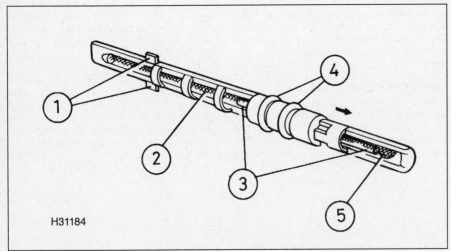

H31184

Cutaway view of typical orifice tube

1 Removal tabs	3 Orifice	5 Outlet filter screen
2 Inlet filter screen	4 O-rings	

Arrow shows direction of refrigerant flow

Air conditioning system control components

So far, we've discussed the main components necessary to enable any air conditioning system to do its job. Although these components are necessary to enable an air conditioning system to work, they do not provide enough control to allow the system to work efficiently. For this reason, all automotive air conditioning systems must have additional control devices which allow monitoring of the system operation and a degree of control to enable the system to operate at optimum efficiency.

Two of the main control devices have already been discussed because they are common to every automotive air conditioning system – namely the compressor clutch, and the expansion valve or orifice tube, depending on the type of system. These devices are used to regulate the flow of refrigerant (and therefore the transfer, and eventual removal of heat) through the air conditioning system.

Regulating the refrigerant flow through the system does not guarantee optimum cooling efficiency, and a number of additional control devices are necessary to improve the efficiency of the system, to protect various system components, and to maintain acceptable driveability of the vehicle with the air conditioning system is operating. These additional components can be divided up into four main groups:

Compressor controls.
Condenser fan controls.
Evaporator controls.
Driveability controls.

Additionally, a high pressure relief valve may be fitted to some systems.

The components described in the following pages are amongst the most widely used components in modern automotive air conditioning systems, but additional components not mentioned here, or variations on those found here may be encountered in some systems. The information given is general, and it's advisable to refer to the appropriate vehicle manufacturer's information for specific details of a particular system.

Compressor controls

Before discussing compressor controls, it's necessary to understand that compressors used in modern vehicle air conditioning systems may either run constantly whenever the air conditioning system is switched on, or may be cycled (switched on and off) according to the requirements of the system.

Most modern constant-running compressor systems use a variable-displacement compressor. With this type of compressor, the refrigerant flow can be controlled without switching the compressor on and off (see *Variable-displacement piston-type compressors*). Note that constant-running compressors still have a compressor clutch in order to allow the compressor to be stopped when the air conditioning system is switched off, and when necessary for safety reasons (eg, low or excessive system pressure).

The compressor can be effectively switched on and off by controlling the power supply to the compressor clutch coil. Switching of the compressor can be used to prevent excessively high or low system pressures, and overcooling, and to protect the compressor itself from damage due to extreme operating conditions. Switching of the compressor is also used to control the refrigerant flow on systems with a cycling compressor.

The most commonly used compressor controls include the following:.

Low pressure cut-out switch.
High pressure cut-out switch.
Trinary switch.
Ambient temperature switch.
Pressure-sensitive (cycling) switch (orifice tube type systems).
Thermal fuse/superheat switch.
Thermostatic switch.
Compressor crankcase pressure control valve (variable displacement compressors).

Various other compressor controls may be used, particularly on modern vehicles with engine management systems, where the compressor clutch is often controlled by the engine management system electronic control unit (ECU). For example, the compressor may have a maximum recommended rotational speed beyond which the internal components may be damaged, so the compressor clutch may be disengaged if the engine speed reaches a level which is likely to damage the compressor. Similarly, if the air conditioning system is switched on, and the driver presses the accelerator pedal fully when the engine speed is low, the compressor clutch may disengaged for a period to increase the engine power available for acceleration.

Let's take a look at the more common compressor controls in more detail.

2

Low pressure cut-out switch

The switch is usually wired in series with the compressor clutch, and is used to stop the compressor if the system pressure falls below a predetermined level, which will usually be due to a refrigerant leak somewhere in the system, a blockage in the refrigerant circuit, or very low temperature. If the refrigerant pressure is low because of a leak, or there is no pressure, compressor oil may have been lost along with the refrigerant, and the compressor may be damaged due to lack of lubrication if it continues to run.

If the refrigerant pressure drops below a pre-determined level, the switch contacts open, stopping the compressor. If the pressure rises above the predetermined level, the switch contacts close, and the compressor is re-activated.

As well as stopping the compressor if there is a refrigerant leak, the switch will also stop the compressor if the ambient temperature falls to a very low level (causing low pressure), when there is a risk of damage to the compressor seals, gaskets and reed valves due to poor oil circulation.

The switch is usually fitted to the high pressure side of the system on expansion valve-type systems, often in the filter/drier or the expansion valve assembly **(see illustration)**. On orifice tube-type systems, the switch is fitted to the low side of the system, usually in the accumulator.

High pressure cut-out switch

This switch is usually wired in series with the compressor clutch, and is used to stop the compressor if the system pressure rises beyond a predetermined level, which will usually be due to a blockage somewhere in the refrigerant circuit, or overheating of the condenser.

If the refrigerant pressure reaches a pre-determined level, the switch contacts open, stopping the compressor. If the pressure drops back below the predetermined level, the switch contacts close, and the compressor is re-activated.

The switch is fitted to the high pressure side of the system, often in the compressor casing **(see illustration)**.

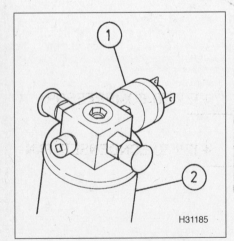

Typical low pressure cut-out switch location – expansion valve system with filter/drier

1   Low pressure cut-out switch
2   Filter/drier

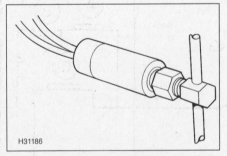

Typical high pressure cut-out switch located in refrigerant line

Trinary switch

This switch is basically a high pressure cut-out switch, low pressure cut-out switch, and a condenser fan switch combined into one assembly **(see illustration)**.

If the system pressure falls, the low pressure switch opens, stopping the compressor. If the system pressure is excessively high, the high pressure switch opens, stopping the compressor. If the condenser temperature rises beyond a preset limit, the fan switch closes, activating the condenser cooling fan.

Trinary switches are common on expansion valve-type systems, and are usually fitted to the filter/drier assembly.

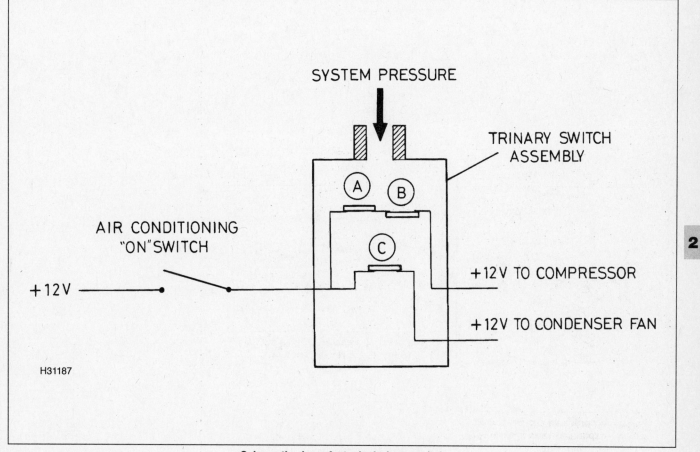

Schematic view of a typical trinary switch

A Low-pressure cut-out switch   B High pressure cut-out switch   C Condenser fan start switch

Ambient temperature switch

The ambient temperature switch measures the outside air temperature, and is used in some systems to prevent compressor operation when the outside air temperature is low. If the compressor is operated in extremely cold conditions, it can cause poor oil circulation, damaging the compressor seals, gaskets and/or valves.

If the ambient temperature drops below the range suitable for compressor operation, the switch opens, preventing current flow to the compressor, which stops the compressor. When the ambient temperature reaches the predetermined minimum operating temperature, the switch contacts close, and the compressor starts again.

The switch is usually located at the front of the engine compartment, often behind the front grille panel, where it can quickly and accurately sense outside air temperature **(see illustration)**.

Pressure-sensitive (cycling) switch (orifice tube type systems)

The switch senses the pressure on the low side of the system, and uses the pressure as an indicator to evaporator temperature **(see illustration)**. The compressor is then cycled on and off by the switch to control the evaporator temperature. Additionally, the switch provides freeze protection, and stops the compressor when the ambient temperature (and hence the system pressure) is low. This switch also usually acts as a low pressure cut-out switch (described previously).

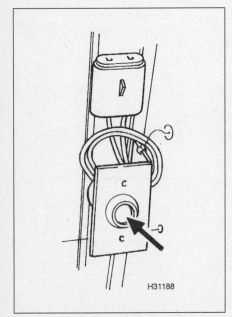

H31188

Typical ambient temperature switch (arrowed)

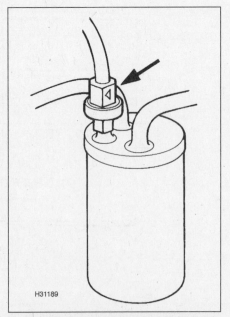

H31189

Typical pressure-sensitive (cycling) switch (arrowed) located in accumulator

Thermal fuse/superheat switch

A thermal fuse and superheat switch are used to stop the compressor in the event of low system pressure. The two components are used on some vehicles (eg, certain Jaguars) instead of a low pressure cut-out switch **(see illustration)**. The superheat switch is located in the rear of the compressor, and is exposed to the flow of cold refrigerant. The switch contacts are normally open, but if a predetermined temperature is reached (due to a reduction in refrigerant flow), the contacts close, earthing the heater circuit in the thermal fuse through the body of the compressor. When the air conditioning circuit is switched on, the thermal fuse and its heater coil receive a 12-volt supply from the battery, and when the superheat switch contacts close, the circuit is completed (earthed) which causes the heater coil to heat the fuse. The heater coil will eventually melt the fuse, which cuts the supply to the compressor coil, stopping the compressor.

The thermal fuse is often mounted on a bracket on the compressor. If the thermal fuse blows, it must be renewed. A blown fuse can usually be recognised from its melted casing.

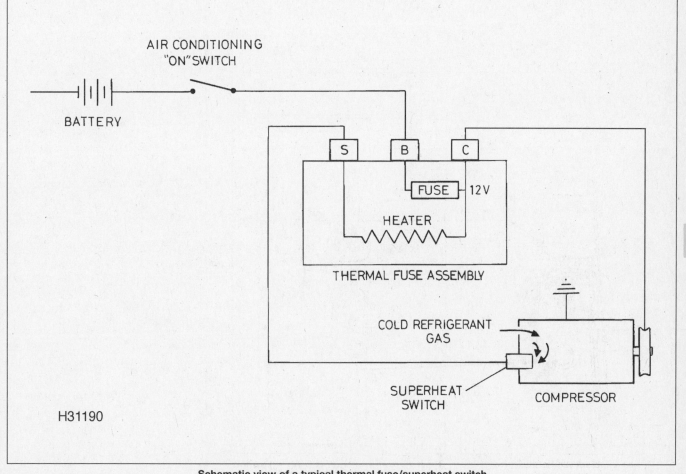

Schematic view of a typical thermal fuse/superheat switch

Thermostatic switch

The thermostatic switch fitted to some systems is used to control the compressor according to the temperature of the evaporator. The switch has a temperature-sensing capillary tube located to sense the evaporator temperature **(see illustration)**. The capillary action will cause the switch contacts to open or close according to the temperature of the evaporator. The switch works within a predetermined temperature range, switching the compressor off at a preset temperature and back on again at another preset temperature. Some switches are adjustable so that the compressor switching can be controlled according to the system and vehicle occupants' requirements.

When the temperature in the evaporator approaches freezing, the thermostatic switch contacts open, disengaging the compressor clutch, which stops the compressor. This allows the temperature in the evaporator to rise (due to the lack of refrigerant flow) until, at the predetermined temperature, the switch contacts close, engaging the compressor clutch, and restarting the compressor.

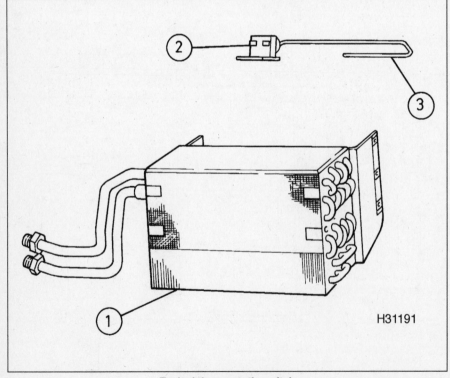

H31191

Typical thermostatic switch

1 Evaporator   2 Thermostatic switch   3 Capillary tube

Compressor crankcase pressure control valve (variable displacement compressors)

This valve is mounted in the rear of the compressor, and regulates the compressor crankcase pressure **(see illustration)**. The crankcase pressure controls the angle of the variable-angle squish-plate, which in turn controls the compressor displacement (see *Variable displacement piston-type compressors*).

The control valve contains a pressure-sensitive diaphragm, which is exposed to pressure on the suction side of the compressor. The diaphragm acts on a valve exposed to the compressor high-side pressure. The diaphragm also controls the opening and closing of a bleed port which is exposed to suction side pressure.

When the temperature of the evaporator decreases, or the speed of the compressor increases (due to engine speed), the low-side pressure (suction) at the compressor decreases. This reduction in pressure is sensed by the control valve, which allows pressure from the high-side of the compressor through the bleed port into the crankcase. The high pressure in the crankcase pushes against the undersides of the compressor pistons, reducing the angle of the squish-plate, and effectively shortening the stroke of the pistons.

When the temperature of the evaporator increases, or the speed of the compressor reduces, the low-side pressure at the compressor increases. The increase in pressure moves the control valve diaphragm to close off the high pressure bleed port into the crankcase. This reduces the crankcase pressure, increasing the angle of the squish-plate, and effectively lengthening the stroke of the pistons.

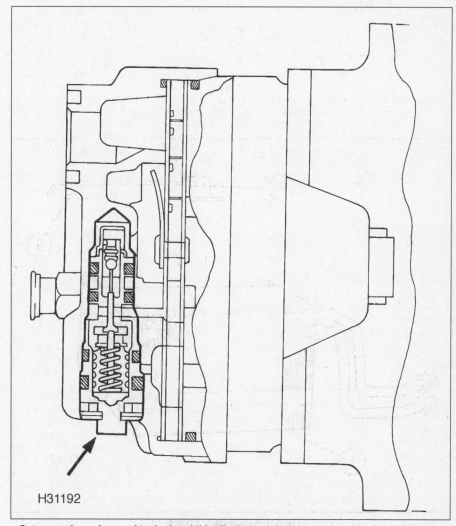

H31192

Cutaway view of rear of typical variable displacement compressor showing crankcase pressure control valve location (arrowed)

2

Condenser fan controls

Most vehicles use an electric cooling fan to ensure an adequate flow of air through the condenser and the cooling system radiator. On vehicles with air conditioning, two fans are often fitted, and they're usually connected to the air conditioning control system and operate when the system is turned on. This ensures an adequate airflow through the condenser at all times, and helps to prevent excessive system pressure.

Although the fan system does not have a direct affect on the operation of the air conditioning system, if a fan does not operate when required, it can rapidly lead to excessive system pressures and temperatures.

The most commonly used condenser fan controls include the following:

Cooling fan switch (located in the engine coolant circuit).
Air conditioning system high pressure fan switch.
Air conditioning system trinary switch.
Air conditioning system 'on' switch.
Pressure-sensitive air conditioning system fan switch.

Further details of each component are given in the following paragraphs.

Cooling system fan temperature switch

This sensor is not part of the air conditioning system, and switches on the cooling fan(s) when the engine coolant reaches a predetermined temperature. The switch interrupts power to the fan(s) when the coolant temperature drops below a second predetermined temperature (usually lower than the switch on temperature). Note that on many vehicles, the cooling fan(s) will run even when the ignition is switched off.

Air conditioning system high pressure fan switch

On some vehicles, a high pressure switch in the air conditioning system refrigerant circuit activates the cooling fan(s) when the refrigerant pressure rises above a pre-determined level, shortly after the compressor starts to operate. When the air conditioning system is switched off, the cooling fan system is controlled purely by the cooling system fan temperature switch. On some vehicles, the air conditioning system high pressure fan switch may provide an input signal to the engine management system.

Air conditioning system trinary switch

On some vehicles, an air conditioning system high pressure fan switch (described previously) is incorporated in the trinary switch (see Compressor controls).

Air conditioning system 'on' switch

Many vehicles have an air conditioning system 'on' fan switch, which activates the fan(s) whenever the air conditioning system is switched on. This ensures that there is always an adequate airflow through the condenser.

Pressure-sensitive air conditioning system fan switch

This type of switch may be encountered on certain vehicles fitted with a variable-displacement compressor (which runs constantly). This switch controls the cooling fan(s) according to the compressor high-side pressure, and is located in the compressor refrigerant discharge line. The switch operates in conjunction with the cooling system fan temperature switch.

Evaporator controls

Note: *The controls described here are used to control the evaporator temperature by directly controlling the refrigerant flow through the evaporator. It's important to note that the evaporator temperature is also effectively controlled by the cycling of the compressor, which indirectly controls the flow of refrigerant through the evaporator. Details of compressor's controls are given earlier in this Chapter.*

Evaporator controls tend to be found on older US specification vehicles with compressors which run constantly. Evaporator controls are rare on European vehicles, although they may be found on some older vehicles such as the Rover SD1 series.

As we've already seen, the refrigerant flow through the evaporator is the key to the efficient operation of an air conditioning system. Sometimes, under certain operating conditions, the condensation which forms on the outside of the evaporator may freeze, which can block the evaporator fins, and reduce the airflow through the evaporator. This reduces the evaporator's cooling ability, and hence the efficiency of the system.

Evaporator controls help to prevent freezing, and help keep the air conditioning system operating efficiently.

The most commonly used evaporator controls include:

Suction throttling valve (STV).
Pilot Operated Absolute Suction Throttling Valve (POA STV).
Valves-In-Receiver (VIR).
Evaporator-Equalised Valves-In-Receiver (EEVIR).
Evaporator Pressure Regulator (EPR) valve.

Suction Throttling Valve (STV)

The suction throttling valve (STV) was used on some early expansion valve type air conditioning systems to control the refrigerant flow leaving the evaporator. In an air conditioning system containing an STV, the compressor is running constantly, as long as the air conditioning system is switched on.

A typical STV opens or closes in response to refrigerant pressure to keep the pressure in the evaporator within a predetermined range. This maintains the evaporator temperature at a level which ensures efficient operation of the air conditioning system without allowing the evaporator to freeze up.

Pilot Operated Absolute Suction Throttling Valve (POA STV)

Most modern STVs are of the pilot operated absolute (POA) type. A POA STV valve is really nothing more than a spring-loaded valve, controlled by an evacuated bellows and needle valve assembly inside a housing (see illustration). The valve operates indepen-dently of atmospheric pressure, and is not affected by altitude changes. By providing an opposing force to evaporator pressure, the valve can maintain the evaporator pressure very accurately (often within a 1 psi/7 kPa range).

Provided the evaporator pressure is above a predetermined level, the POA STV valve remains open to allow refrigerant to flow freely out of the evaporator. When the pressure drops below the predetermined level, the valve closes, and the refrigerant flow from the evaporator is restricted. The pressure in the evaporator then increases, which raises the temperature and prevents possible freezing on the outside of the evaporator. The opening and closing cycle of the valve continues as long as the compressor is running.

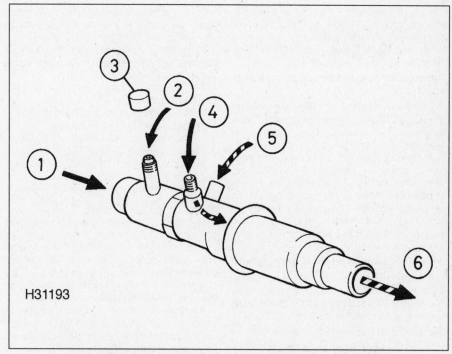

H31193

Typical Pilot Operated Absolute Suction Throttling Valve (POA STV)

1 Refrigerant flow from evaporator
2 Service valve
3 Protective cap
4 Liquid bleed line connection
5 Expansion valve equaliser line connection (not used on all valves)
6 Refrigerant flow to compressor

2

Valves-In-Receiver (VIR)

A valves-in-receiver (VIR) assembly is a combined expansion valve, pilot-operated absolute suction throttling valve (POA STV), and filter/drier in one unit. The unit is usually mounted near the evaporator (see illustration).

In a VIR unit, the temperature-sensing bulb and capillary tube for the expansion valve are eliminated because the diaphragm end of the expansion valve is directly exposed to the refrigerant vapour entering the VIR unit from the evaporator outlet.

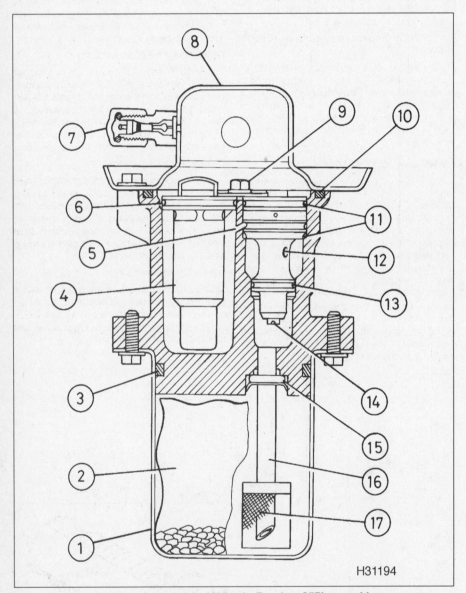

H31194

Cutaway view of typical Valve-In-Receiver (VIR) assembly

1 Receiver (filter)/drier casing
2 Desiccant bag
3 Valve housing-to-receiver O-ring
4 POA valve capsule
5 Equaliser port
6 POA valve O-ring
7 Service valve
8 Inlet connector casing
9 Valve capsule securing screw and washer assembly
10 Inlet connector casing-to-valve housing O-ring
11 Expansion valve upper O-rings
12 Expansion valve capsule
13 Expansion valve lower O-ring
14 Expansion valve inlet
15 Liquid pick-up tube O-ring
16 Liquid pick-up tube
17 Pick-up tube filter screen

Evaporator-Equalised Valves-In-Receiver (EEVIR)

The evaporator-equalised valves-in-receiver unit is a modified version of the VIR unit (described previously) which has a redesigned expansion valve in order to eliminate temperature fluctuations in the system which occur under certain operating conditions. The expansion valve is also modified so that it is always partially open instead of closing completely, which helps to prevent freezing at the expansion valve (which will block the refrigerant flow and stop the system from operating).

Evaporator Pressure Regulator (EPR) valve

The evaporator pressure regulator (EPR) valve is normally fitted to the inlet port of the compressor **(see illustration)**. The valve maintains the evaporator outlet pressure within predetermined limits. An EPR valve performs the same function as the suction throttling valve described previously.

Driveability controls

An air conditioning compressor takes a significant amount of power to run (on average between 7 and 11 kW/ 10 and 15 hp of engine power), and the effect of compressor operation, in conjunction with other demands placed on the engine, can impose loads which reduce vehicle performance. This is a significant problem on vehicles with small capacity engines.

Driveability controls are used to control the operation of the compressor to relieve the load on the engine under conditions when driveability may suffer. These controls do not usually affect the cooling performance of the air conditioning system.

Note: *On most modern vehicles fitted with engine management systems, the air conditioning compressor clutch is controlled by the engine management electronic control unit (ECU). The compressor is controlled according to the information received from the various engine management system sensors, to ensure that the driveability of the vehicle does not suffer. This reduces the need for separate driveability controls.*

Time delay relay

A time delay relay is sometimes used to delay the engagement of the compressor for a few seconds after engine start-up if the air conditioning is switched on.

Wide-open throttle switch

A wide-open throttle switch is sometimes used on vehicles with small capacity engines. The switch is operated by the throttle linkage. When the throttle pedal is fully depressed, the switch activates a relay which interrupts the compressor clutch circuit. This reduces the load on the engine, and improves acceleration.

Closed throttle switch

A closed throttle switch is sometimes used on vehicle with small capacity engines. The switch is operated by the throttle linkage, and interrupts the compressor clutch circuit to prevent the risk of the compressor load stalling the engine when the throttle is closed under overrun conditions.

Low vacuum switch

Low vacuum switches are used on some vehicles to interrupt the operation of the air conditioning compressor when engine loads are heavy, resulting in low vacuum in the inlet manifold.

2

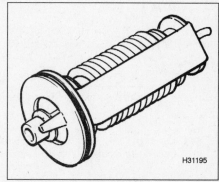

H31195

Typical Evaporator Pressure Regulator (EPR) valve

Power steering pressure switch

On a vehicle with a small capacity engine and power steering, under normal driving conditions, the power steering has little effect on the performance of the vehicle. However, during parking manoeuvres, the power steering system imposes its heaviest loads on the engine. When parking, the engine speed and power output are usually low, and so compressor operation is likely to reduce the engine power available even further, which may cause rough idling and stalling.

To prevent these problems, some vehicles are fitted with a power steering pressure switch, which disengages the compressor whenever the power steering hydraulic pressure exceeds a predetermined level.

Some vehicles are equipped with a more sophisticated version of this system where the switch sends a signal to the engine management system. The engine management ECU can then adjust the engine idle speed to compensate for the higher steering loads, without the need to disengage the compressor.

Power brake switch

On a vehicle with a small capacity engine, if the air conditioning compressor is running when the brakes are applied, it's possible that the engine may stall, which could be potentially dangerous. A power brake switch may be fitted to disengage the compressor under certain circumstances when the brakes are applied, to prevent the possibility of engine stalling.

Engine coolant high temperature switch

The air conditioning condenser is usually positioned in front of the engine cooling system radiator. The air conditioning system transfers heat to the air passing through the condenser, which then has to pass through the radiator. When the ambient temperature is high, the already heated air passing over the radiator is unable to carry away sufficient heat from the engine coolant, and overheating can result.

To prevent the possibility of overheating, some vehicles are equipped with a coolant temperature switch which disengages the compressor clutch when the coolant temperature exceeds a predetermined level.

Constant run relay

Some vehicles are equipped with a constant run relay which is controlled by the engine management system, and is used to maintain idle quality. The relay prevents compressor cycling when the engine is idling, for a predetermined period after normal driving. If the engine is left idling for an extended time, the relay returns the compressor to its normal cycling mode for a short time, to prevent the evaporator from freezing up.

Compressor delay timer

This device is sometimes used on vehicles equipped with an engine management system. When the engine is idling (or running below a predetermined speed), and the air conditioning system is switched on, the timer delays the engagement of the compressor clutch for a few seconds whilst the engine idle speed is raised to compensate for the additional load. The compressor clutch is engaged as soon as the engine idle speed has stabilised.

Anti-dieseling relay

Some engines have a tendency to run on or 'diesel' after the ignition is switched off. To prevent this, on some vehicles the compressor is used to prevent dieseling. As soon as the ignition is switched off, the compressor clutch is engaged for a few seconds. This additional load stalls the engine and prevents dieseling.

High pressure relief valve

Many systems incorporate a high pressure relief valve, although a few systems use a disc which will burst when a pre-determined pressure is reached. The valve or disc is fitted to the high pressure side of the system, and is used as a safety device in the event of excessive pressure in the system. Most valves will close when the pressure has dropped to a safe level. Any excess pressure is likely to be due to an overheated condenser or an overcharge of refrigerant.

The valve is often located on the receiver/drier (expansion valve type systems) or on the compressor, usually in a safe place, so that there is no risk of refrigerant being discharged towards anyone working on the vehicle.

If the valve opens for any reason, the system will require recharging with refrigerant and compressor oil.

Refrigerants

As we discussed in Chapter 1, there are two refrigerants commonly used in vehicle air conditioning systems, known as R12 and R134a. Other types of refrigerant may be used if the system is serviced, but R12 and R134a are currently the only refrigerants which have been approved by the vehicle manufacturers for use in their air conditioning systems **(see illustration)**.

At this stage, it's important to point out that the components used in most air conditioning systems are designed specifically to be used with either R12 refrigerant, or R134a refrigerant, but **not** both. R12 system components and refrigerant must **never** be used in an R134a system, and *vice versa*. There are three main reasons for this:

1) *R12 systems use a mineral-based compressor oil, whereas R134a systems use synthetic PAG oil (see Compressor oils). If the wrong refrigerant is used, it will not mix with the oil in the system, resulting in a lack of lubrication, and serious damage to the compressor.*
2) *The seals and flexible hoses used in R134a systems are specially designed to prevent the extremely small R134a molecules from escaping from the system (the molecules are small enough to pass through a normal hose). If R134a is used in an R12 system, the refrigerant will leak out.*
3) *In general, R134a systems operate at higher pressures than R12 systems. If R134a is used in a system designed for R12, the higher pressures may cause damage to components (particularly the compressor) and seals.*

Now let's look at the two refrigerants in more detail.

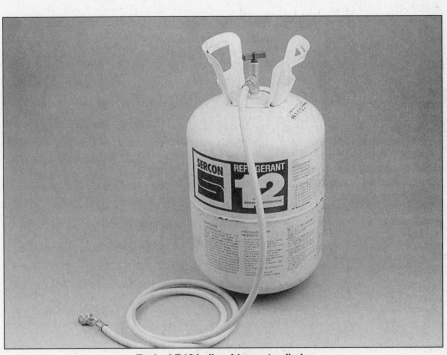

Typical R12 bulk refrigerant cylinder

2

R12

General

- R12 refrigerant is a CFC (ChloroFluoro Carbon) and has been used since it was first discovered in the 1930s.
- An air conditioning system which uses R12 refrigerant can be identified from its screw-on service port connections (see Chapter 6).

Advantages

- R12 is non-flammable.
- R12 is non-poisonous in small quantities.
- R12 mixes with mineral oil (mineral oil can be used to lubricate the compressor).

Disadvantages

- R12 destroys ozone.
- R12 is a greenhouse gas.
- In the presence of an open flame, it produces phosgene (mustard gas) which is deadly to humans.

R134a

General

- R134a refrigerant has been used instead of R12 since around 1992.
- An air conditioning system which uses R134a refrigerant can be identified from its snap-on service port connections (see Chapter 6).

Advantages

- R134a is non-flammable.
- R134a is non-poisonous in small quantities.
- R134a is ozone-friendly.
- The cost of R134a is low compared to that of R12.

Disadvantages

- R134a is a greenhouse gas (less damaging than R12).
- In the presence of an open flame, it produces hydrogen fluoride (HF) gas which is deadly to humans.
- R134a needs special barrier refrigerant hoses to keep refrigerant in (due to the very small size of R134a molecules) and moisture out (the compressor oil is very hygroscopic).
- R134a does not mix with mineral oil, so a special oil (PAG oil) must be used in the compressor. This oil is very expensive and hygroscopic (see Compressor oils).

Alternative refrigerants

There are numerous alternatives to R12 and R134a on the market for use when servicing air conditioning systems, but at the time of writing, R12 and R134a were the only refrigerants approved by the vehicle manufacturers for use in their systems.

It's strongly recommended that only the manufacturer's specified refrigerant is used during any service operations (see Chapter 6).

Bear in mind that if some of the alternative refrigerants are introduced into equipment designed for handling R12 or R134a (even dual circuit machines designed to handle both R12 and R134a), the equipment may be contaminated. It's strongly recommended that the refrigerant in the system is identified before connecting refrigerant handling equipment – see Chapter 6.

Compressor oils

All compressors need lubricating [...] protect the internal components and [...] case of rotary vane compressors, to p[...] sealing action. Without oil, a compresso[...] fail very quickly, and this could prove to b[...] very expensive!

Although the purpose of the oil is purely to lubricate the compressor, the oil and the refrigerant mix together, and are pumped around the system by the compressor. This means that although a high proportion of the oil will be in the compressor at any one time, a proportion of the oil will be circulating around the other system components. This in turn means that if there is a refrigerant leak, some oil will also be lost from the system.

Two different types of oil are used in automotive air conditioning systems, and the type of oil used depends on the type of refrigerant used in the system.

R12 refrigerant mixes with mineral oil, so a mineral oil can be used to lubricate the compressor. Most compressors use the same grade of mineral oil, but a number of grades of oil are available. The grade of oil recommended

[...] viso[...]
[...] viscos[...]
[...] requireme[...]
[...] diluting affec[...]uld
Always use the [...]
the compressor ma[...]

Note: *Compressor oi[...] are very hygroscopic – ie, [...] To prevent problems, [...] containers must always be tightly sealed, and should not be left open to atmosphere. Some compressor oil manufacturers recommend that the oil is discarded if it is left open to the atmosphere for more than 20 minutes! Similarly, whenever system components are disconnected, the open pipes and components should be sealed immediately (cover or plug the openings) to minimise the entry of moisture.*

Chapter 3
Typical air conditioning systems

3

Contents

Introduction . . . . .3•1
High and low sides of the air conditioning system . . . . .3•2
   High side . . . . .3•3
   Low side . . . . .3•3
Manually-controlled air conditioning systems . . . . .3•4
   Expansion valve system . . . . .3•4

Orifice tube (or 'accumulator') system .3•5
Suction Throttling Valve (STV) system .3•6
Valves-In-Receiver (VIR) system . . . . .3•7
Evaporator Pressure Regulator (EPR) system . . . . .3•8
Automatic air conditioning/climate control systems . . . . .3•9

Introduction

Now that we're familiar with how an air conditioning system works, and we've discussed the various components used in Chapters 1 and 2, let's take a look at how the components work together in a typical modern system.

High and low sides of the air conditioning system

Before looking at the individual components of an air conditioning system, it's important to realise that all systems have a high and low pressure side. The dividing line for the two sides always occurs at the same point in the system, regardless of the type of system, ie, between the compressor and the expansion valve or orifice tube **(see illustrations)**.

The compressor raises the pressure and the temperature so that the refrigerant can condense and release heat as it moves through the condenser. A pressure-differential (actually a pressure drop) is created at the expansion valve or orifice tube which is one of the dividing points between the high side and low side.

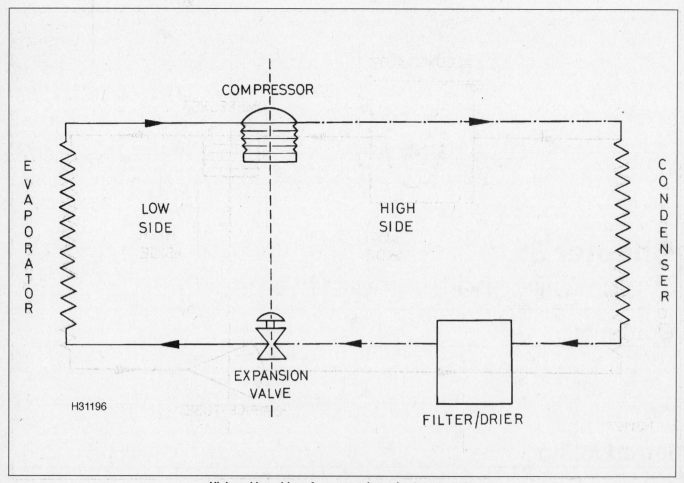

COMPRESSOR

EVAPORATOR

LOW SIDE

HIGH SIDE

CONDENSER

EXPANSION VALVE

FILTER/DRIER

H31196

High and low sides of an expansion valve type system

High side

The high side is the portion of the system where the refrigerant is at a high pressure and temperature. The high side runs from the outlet (or discharge) side of the compressor, through the condenser and, where applicable, the filter/drier, to the expansion valve or orifice tube (as applicable).

Low side

The low side is the remaining half of the system. On this side, from the expansion valve or orifice tube, through the evaporator and accumulator (where applicable) to the inlet (or suction) side of the compressor, the refrigerant is in a low pressure, low temperature state.

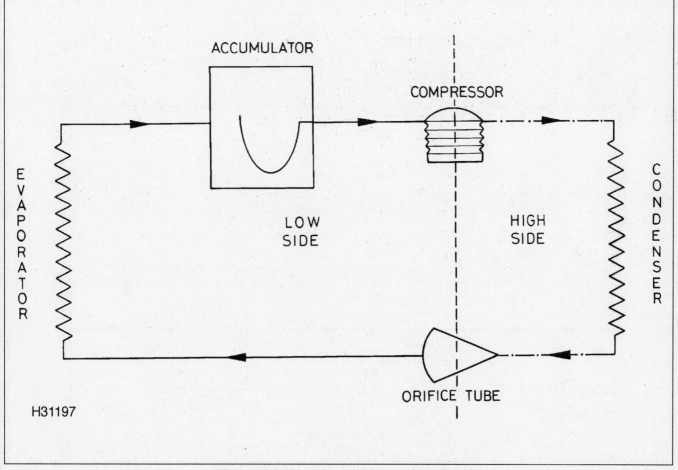

High and low sides of an orifice tube type system

Manually-controlled air conditioning systems

Now we'll take a look at some typical air conditioning systems in more detail. The systems described here rely on manual control, ie, the temperature inside the vehicle is controlled manually by the vehicle occupants using the air conditioning and heater controls provided.

We'll look at the following systems:

- *Expansion valve system.*
- *Orifice tube (or 'accumulator') system.*
- *Suction Throttling Valve (STV) system.*
- *Valves-In-Receiver (VIR) system.*
- *Evaporator Pressure Regulator (EPR) system.*

By far the most common systems used in modern vehicles are the expansion valve system and the orifice tube (or 'accumulator') system. The other systems are briefly described here because they may be encountered on some older vehicles and on some imported US specification vehicles.

Note that with all types of air conditioning system, either a constant-running or a cycling compressor may be used (see Chapter 2), and the systems may be designed to use either R12 or R134a refrigerant (see Chapter 6, *R12 and R134a service valves*, for details of how to identify which refrigerant the system is designed to use).

Expansion valve system

On an expansion valve system, the compressor raises the pressure and temperature of the refrigerant, and pumps the high pressure vapour into the condenser **(see illustration)**. The refrigerant condenses inside the condenser to a high pressure liquid. The liquid refrigerant then passes through a filter/drier on the high side of the system before reaching the expansion valve. The filter/drier cleans the refrigerant and removes any moisture before the refrigerant reaches the expansion valve. The expansion valve reduces the pressure and temperature of the refrigerant so that the high pressure liquid leaves the expansion valve as a low pressure mixture of liquid and vapour. The flow of refrigerant through the expansion valve is controlled according to the temperature of the refrigerant entering the evaporator, and this ensures that all the refrigerant is boiled to a vapour in the evaporator before it reaches the compressor. The compressor draws in the low pressure refrigerant vapour from the evaporator, and the cycle begins again. Further details of how the individual components work are given in Chapter 2.

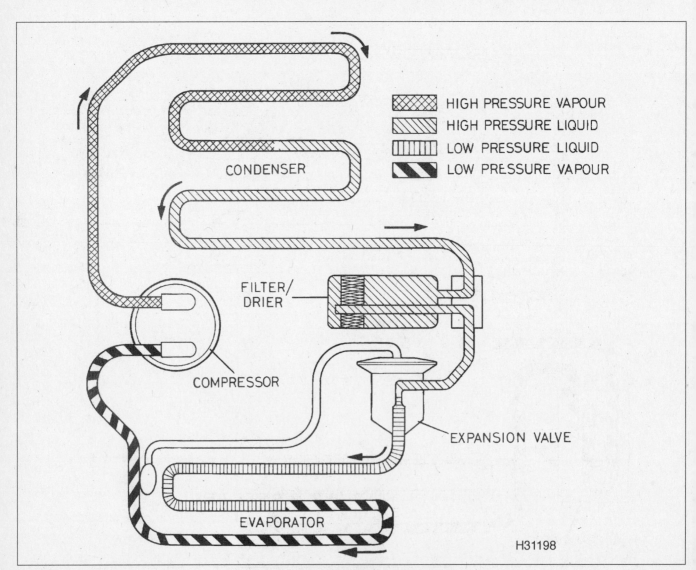

Layout of a typical expansion valve system

Orifice tube (or 'accumulator') system

On an orifice tube system, the compressor raises the pressure and temperature of the refrigerant, and pumps the high pressure vapour into the condenser (see illustration). The refrigerant condenses inside the condenser to a high pressure liquid. The liquid refrigerant then passes through the orifice tube where its pressure and temperature are reduced, so that the refrigerant leaves the orifice tube as a low pressure liquid. The liquid refrigerant enters the evaporator, where most of it is boiled to a vapour, with a small proportion of liquid remaining. The refrigerant mixture then passes to the accumulator on the low side of the system, where any remaining refrigerant liquid is boiled to a vapour before being passed to the compressor. The compressor draws in the low pressure refrigerant vapour from the accumulator, and the cycle begins again. Further details of how the individual components work are given in Chapter 2.

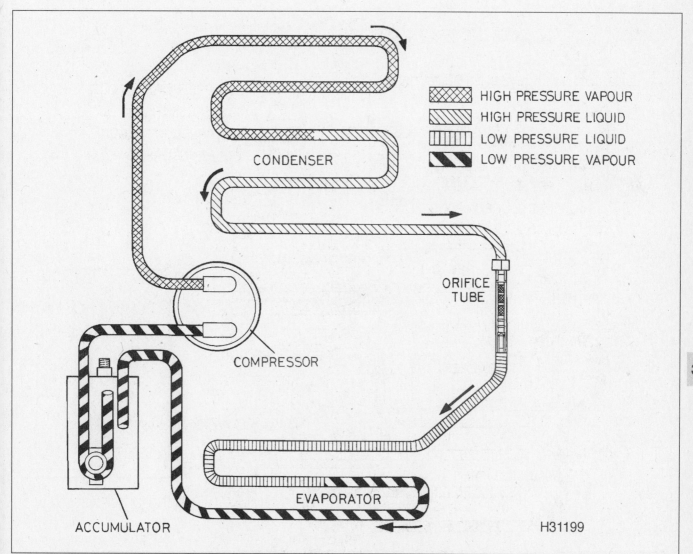

HIGH PRESSURE VAPOUR
HIGH PRESSURE LIQUID
LOW PRESSURE LIQUID
LOW PRESSURE VAPOUR

CONDENSER

ORIFICE TUBE

COMPRESSOR

ACCUMULATOR

EVAPORATOR

H31199

Layout of a typical orifice tube (or 'accumulator') system

3

Suction Throttling Valve (STV) system

Suction throttling valve (STV) systems may be encountered on some older vehicles, but this system has been largely superceded. The system is a variation on the thermostatic expansion valve system. A thermostatic expansion valve is used to reduce the pressure and temperature of the refrigerant, but with this type of system, the compressor runs constantly (which provided a constant drain on engine power) as long as the air conditioning system is switched on, and the evaporator temperature is controlled by the STV. The STV is mounted on the outlet side of the evaporator **(see illustration)**. A typical STV opens or closes in response to refrigerant pressure to keep the pressure in the evaporator within a predetermined range. This maintains the evaporator temperature at a level which ensures efficient operation of the air conditioning system without allowing the evaporator to freeze up.

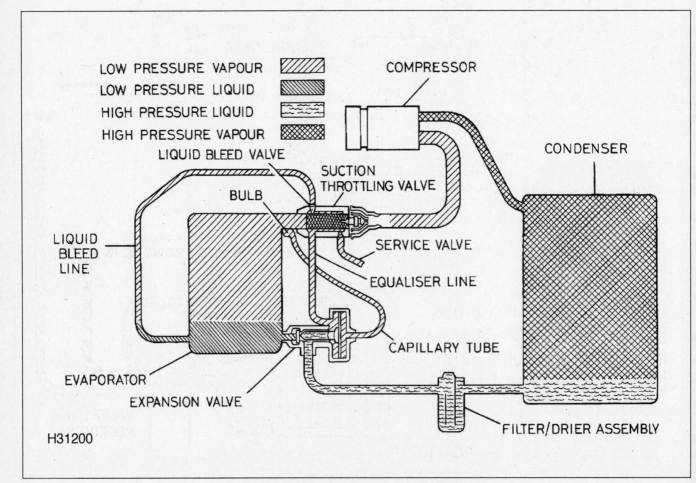

Layout of a typical Suction Throttling Valve (STV) system

Valves-In-Receiver (VIR) system

This system was used on some older General Motors vehicles (particularly US specification vehicles) and is a variation on the suction throttling valve (STV) system. The thermostatic expansion valve and STV are mounted in the same housing as the filter/drier (also known as a receiver/drier) **(see illustration)**. This combined unit is located in the high pressure side of the system, between the condenser and the evaporator. The VIR unit controls the refrigerant flow to the evaporator, and the compressor runs constantly as long as the air conditioning system is switched on.

3

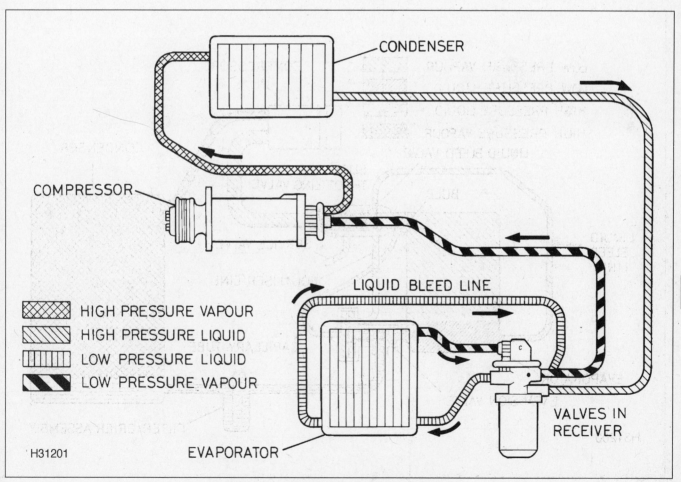

CONDENSER

COMPRESSOR

LIQUID BLEED LINE

VALVES IN RECEIVER

EVAPORATOR

	HIGH PRESSURE VAPOUR
	HIGH PRESSURE LIQUID
	LOW PRESSURE LIQUID
	LOW PRESSURE VAPOUR

H31201

Layout of a typical Valve-In-Receiver (VIR) system

Evaporator Pressure Regulator (EPR) system

This system is used exclusively on certain US specification Chrysler vehicles. The system operates in a similar way to a suction throttling valve system, but the evaporator pressure regulator (EPR) is located inside the compressor inlet **(see illustration)**. The EPR senses the pressure of the refrigerant entering the compressor, and opens or closes to control the refrigerant flow through the compressor, thereby also controlling the evaporator temperature.

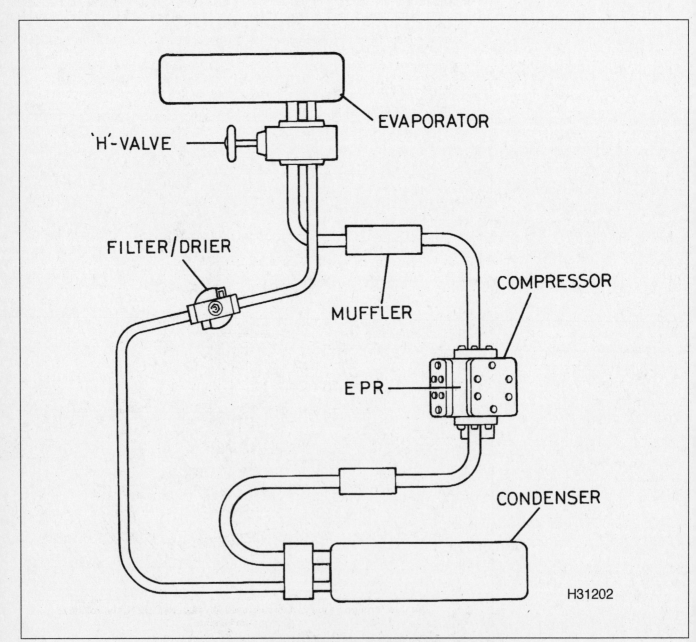

EVAPORATOR

'H'-VALVE

FILTER/DRIER

MUFFLER

COMPRESSOR

EPR

CONDENSER

H31202

Layout of a typical Evaporator Pressure Regulator (EPR) system

Automatic air conditioning/climate control systems

Automatic air conditioning systems are usually integrated with the vehicle heating system to provide an automatic climate control system. These systems will automatically maintain a preset level of heating or cooling, and therefore a constant temperature according to the requirements of the vehicle occupants. There are a large number of different types of automatic system available, and vehicle manufacturers tend to design their own systems to suit particular vehicle models.

Automatic systems use the same basic air conditioning system components as a conventional air conditioning system, but additional compressor controls are normally used, and the system is often under the overall control of an electronic control unit (ECU); either a separate climate control ECU, or sometimes the engine management ECU.

Sensors located inside and/or outside the vehicle allow the automatic system to sense the in-vehicle temperature and/or the outside air temperature. The system then adjusts the level of heating and/or cooling as necessary to maintain the temperature inside the vehicle at the level selected by the occupants.

The temperature inside the vehicle is controlled by using control devices to open and close various flaps within the system air passages, and also to vary the speed of the heater matrix/evaporator blower fan. For example, on some systems blend flaps may be located in the casing between the heater matrix and the evaporator. If more heat is required to raise the temperature, the blend flaps are opened to allow more heat from the heater matrix to reach the passenger compartment. If more cooling is required to reduce the temperature, the flaps move to allow less warm air from the heater matrix, and more cool air from the evaporator to enter **(see illustrations)**.

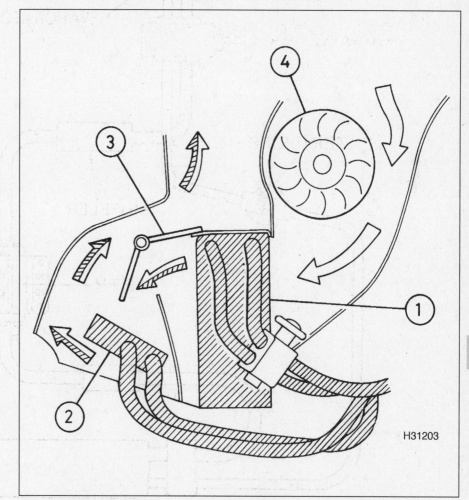

H31203

Air flow through heater/evaporator housing with temperature control set to maximum heating

1 Evaporator
2 Heater matrix
3 Air blend flap
4 Heater blower motor/evaporator fan

3

Many automatic systems have a self-diagnostic system which stores details of any system faults as fault codes in the system electronic control unit (ECU) memory, or in some cases in the engine management electronic control unit (ECU) memory (see Chapter 7).

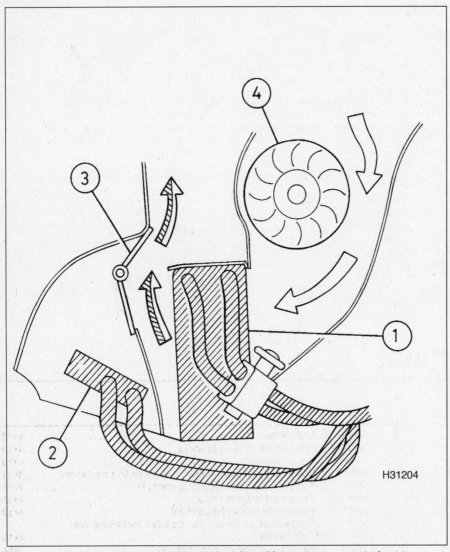

H31204

Air flow through heater/evaporator housing with temperature control set to maximum cooling

1 *Evaporator*
2 *Heater matrix*
3 *Air blend flap*
4 *Heater blower motor/evaporator fan*

Chapter 4
Tools and equipment

Contents

Introduction . . . . .4•1
What tools are needed? . . . . .4•2
   Personal safety equipment . . . . .4•2
   Manifold (test) gauge set . . . . .4•3
   Vacuum pump . . . . .4•6
   Refrigerant recovery machine .4•7
   Refrigerant cylinders . . . . .4•7
   Refrigerant comparator (slide rule type) . . . . .4•8
   Accurate thermometer . . . . .4•9
   Leak detection equipment . . . . .4•9
   Liquid refrigerant charging cylinder . . . . .4•11
   Accurate scales . . . . .4•12

Multimeter . . . . .4•12
Compressor oil level dipsticks . . . . .4•12
Compressor oil . . . . .4•13
Oxygen-free nitrogen (OFN) pressure testing equipment . . . . . .4•13
Refrigerant reclaim (recycling) machine . . . . .4•13
Refrigerant cylinder heater . . . . .4•13
Component flushing equipment . . . . .4•13
Compressor oil injector (for use when recharging with
   refrigerant) . . . . .4•13
Electronic refrigerant gas analyser . . . . .4•14
Spring-lock coupling release tool kit . . . . .4•14
Orifice tube removal tool . . . . .4•14

4

Introduction

In the previous Chapters, we've discussed the basic theory of air conditioning and looked at how the various air conditioning components work together to form an efficient system. As we've seen, once the basic principles are understood, there's no great mystery to air conditioning, and no 'black art'.

However, when we come to carry out work on an air conditioning system, it's essential to have access to certain purpose-built special tools and equipment. It's not possible to improvise this equipment, and without it no attempt should be made to carry out any servicing or diagnostic work.

This Chapter discusses the various special tools and equipment necessary to successfully carry out work on a vehicle air conditioning system.

What tools are needed?

A large range of air conditioning tools and equipment is available from many different manufacturers, ranging from simple portable manually-operated pumps and refrigerant recovery machines to fully-integrated electronically controlled refrigerant handling machines. As when buying any tools, it always pays to buy the best equipment available within your budget, but bear in mind that the most expensive equipment won't necessarily be the most suited to your needs.

Always ensure that you read the relevant manufacturer's information fully before considering making a purchase, and if possible speak to other air conditioning specialists who may have used similar equipment. Bear in mind that you will almost certainly need the use of two complete sets of refrigerant handling equipment; one for use with R12 refrigerant, and one for use with R134a refrigerant – refrigerant cross-contamination can be a serious and expensive problem. A few manufacturers produce dual circuit refrigerant handling machines which are capable of handling both R12 and R134a – these machines should have two sets of recovery and charging equipment, which are completely isolated from each other to avoid cross-contamination (a common set of refrigerant scales, and a single vacuum pump are normally used in these machines, as there is no risk of contamination when weighing refrigerant or evacuating a system).

At this stage, it's important to point out that there are a large number of aftermarket replacement refrigerants on the market, which are neither R12 or R134a. If theses gases are introduced into a refrigerant handling machine (even a dual circuit machine) which is designed for use with R12 or R134a, it may contaminate both the machine and the refrigerant cylinder in which its collected. It's strongly recommended that the refrigerant in a system is identified before connecting refrigerant handling equipment – refer to Chapter 6 for further details.

Most manufacturers produce refrigerant handling and processing equipment which combines several components into one unit, for example, integrated recovery, evacuation, recycling and recharging equipment. Some of this equipment is fully automated. Even if you intend to use such equipment, it's still beneficial to understand how each individual part of the equipment works. The following list and the details provided for each component in this Chapter refer to basic separate tools, although much of the information will apply equally to the component parts of integrated handling equipment.

So, what equipment is needed to carry out work on a vehicle air conditioning system? In addition to the normal tools required to carry out any work on a vehicle (a set of short spanners will prove invaluable when trying to gain access to some well-hidden air conditioning components), the following list gives a guide to the special items required. The list is by no means exhaustive, but shows the minimum basic equipment which will be required to carry out basic fault diagnosis work, leak testing, refrigerant recovery (system discharging) and recharging work. Bear in mind that many refrigerant handling machines incorporate units such as a recovery machine, charging equipment, vacuum pump, manifold gauges, scales, etc, into a single integrated unit.

- *Personal safety equipment (non-absorbent gloves, protective goggles, protective workshop coat or overalls, safety shoes or boots)*
- *Manifold (test) gauge set and hoses*
- *Vacuum pump*
- *Refrigerant recovery machine*
- *Bulk refrigerant cylinders (R12 and R134a)*
- *Waste refrigerant cylinder*
- *Refrigerant comparator (slide rule type)*
- *Accurate thermometer*
- *Leak detection equipment*
- *Liquid refrigerant charging cylinder*
- *Accurate scales*
- *Multimeter*
- *Compressor oil level dipsticks*
- *Compressor oil*
- *Oxygen-Free Nitrogen (OFN) pressure testing equipment*

The following additional equipment is almost certain to be required at some stage if frequent servicing, repair and fault diagnosis work is to be carried out on a range of vehicle types:

- *Refrigerant recycling machine – incorporated into most refrigerant handling machines*
- *Refrigerant recycling cylinder*
- *Refrigerant cylinder heater*
- *Component flushing equipment*
- *Compressor oil injector (for use when recharging with refrigerant)*
- *Electronic refrigerant analyser (expensive, and not essential, but a worthwhile investment)*
- *Spring-lock coupling release tool kit*
- *Orifice tube removal tool*

Now let's take a look at the various equipment in more detail.

Personal safety equipment

The importance of safety cannot be overstressed when working on an air conditioning system. If refrigerant comes into contact with the skin or eyes, it can cause serious and possibly permanent injury. Additionally, some compressor oils are toxic, and can be absorbed through the skin.

It's essential to wear protective goggles (wrap-around type), non-absorbent gloves (such as surgical gloves – **not** thick gardening gloves or gauntlets, which may be absorbent), and a protective coat or overalls. Don't be tempted to work with rolled-up sleeves – there's little point in wearing gloves if the skin on your arms is exposed!

As when carrying out any work in a workshop environment, it's a wise precaution to wear safety shoes or boots – refrigerant cylinders are heavy, and toes are fragile!

Refer to Chapter 5 for further information on safety.

Manifold (test) gauge set

The manifold gauge set is without question the most important tool used when working with air conditioning systems. A gauge set will be required to carry out nearly all servicing and fault diagnosis work **(see illustration)**.

Manifold gauges allow the system high side and low side pressures to be measured which, as we will see in Chapter 6, is essential information for determining whether the system is operating correctly, and for fault diagnosis. Any work involving discharging or charging the system refrigerant is also done via manifold gauges. Manifold gauges allow the refrigerant circuit to be opened in much the same way as a key allows a door to be opened. If the door is locked and you don't have the key, the door can't be opened without the risk of damage and/or injury.

Because the high and low side pressures must be compared in order to determine whether the system is operating correctly, gauge sets are designed to allow both the high and low side pressures to be read at the same time.

The following paragraphs explain the operation of the manifold gauge set in more detail.

Manifold gauges for R12 and R134a systems

Manifold gauges for R134a systems work in exactly the same way as R12 gauges, but the same set of gauges can't be used for both types of system. R12 and R134a gauge sets use completely different connectors and hoses. Gauge sets are marked to indicate which type of system they're designed for, and if a gauge set is marked 'for R134a use only', that's exactly what it means – **do not** try to use a set of R134a gauges on an R12 system, and don't try to use a set of R12 gauges on an R134a system either.

R12 gauge hoses are usually plain colours (red, blue, and yellow – see *Hoses*), whereas R134a gauge hoses usually have a black stripe running the length of each hose.

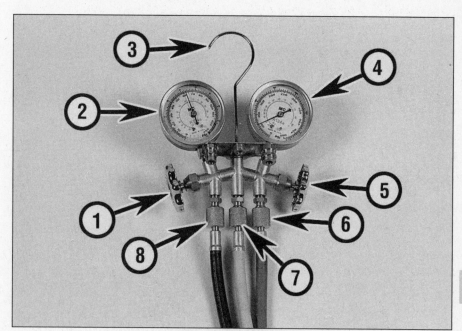

Manifold (test) gauge set

1 A hand valve for the low side of the system
2 A gauge for the low side of the system
3 A hook to suspend the gauge set when working on a vehicle
4 A gauge for the high side of the system
5 A hand valve for the high side of the system

6 A valve for connecting the high side service hose
7 A service valve for connecting devices such as refrigerant cylinders, vacuum pumps and refrigerant recovery machines to the system
8 A valve for connecting the low side service hose

4

The low side gauge

The low side gauge, which is most easily identified by the BLUE housing, hand valve and hose, is used to measure the low side pressure at the service port(s) provided on the low side of the system by the vehicle manufacturer. The low side gauge is sometimes called a compound gauge because it has a dual purpose: to indicate either *pressure* or *vacuum*.

A typical low side gauge pressure scale will read from 0 to between 130 and 160 pounds per square inch (psi), or 0 to approximately 900 to 1100 kPa, in a clockwise direction. A typical vacuum scale will read from 0 to 30 inches of mercury (in Hg), or 0 to 760 mm of mercury (mm Hg), in an anti-clockwise direction **(see illustration)**.

The high side gauge

The high side gauge, which is most easily identified by the RED housing, hand valve and hose, is used to measure the high side pressure at the service port(s) provided on the high side of the system.

A typical high side gauge pressure scale will read from 0 to around 500 psi (0 to 3500 kPa) in a clockwise direction.

Manifold hand valves

The purpose of the manifold is to control refrigerant flow. Once the manifold gauges are connected to the system, pressure is indicated on both gauges constantly, provided the system is operating normally.

During testing, both hand valves should always be closed (turned fully clockwise); even though the valves are closed, the high and low side pressures are still indicated on the respective gauges. The valves do not prevent refrigerant from reaching the gauges, their purpose is to isolate the high and low sides of the system from the central service port on the manifold.

When both hand valves are closed or when either one of the valves is open, the low and high side gauges will give accurate readings. However, when both valves are open, the gauge readings are not accurate because high side pressure bleeds into the low side of the manifold, and influences the low side gauge reading, also giving an inaccurate reading on the high side gauge.

⚠️ *Warning: NEVER OPEN THE HIGH SIDE HAND VALVE WHILE THE AIR CONDITIONING SYSTEM IS OPERATING. High pressure refrigerant will force its way through the high side of the manifold test gauge and into the service hose. If the service hose is not connected to anything, this will vent high pressure refrigerant into the atmosphere. If the service hose is connected to a refrigerant cylinder, the pressure can be high enough to burst the cylinder safety valve fitting, or even rupture the cylinder, resulting in possible damage and injury.*

Hoses

Manifold gauge hoses are always colour-coded to avoid confusion when connecting the gauges to an air conditioning system. R12 gauge hoses are always solid blue (low side), solid red (high side) and solid yellow (service hose). R134a hoses are also blue, red and yellow, but often have a black stripe running the length of each hose.

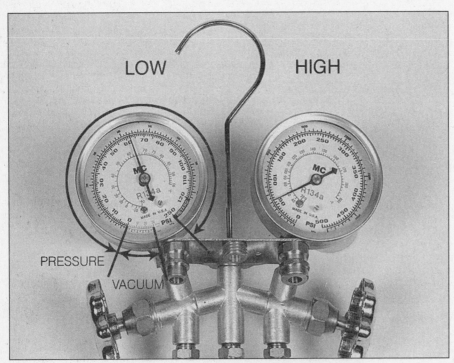

Low side and high side manifold gauges

R134a hoses have different service fittings to those used on R12 hoses. R134a hoses have snap-on connectors, whereas R12 hoses have screw-on connectors. High and low side hoses also have different size fittings, so that the high side of a system cannot accidentally be connected to the low-side gauge, and *vice versa*.

R134a hoses are lined with a special nylon barrier material to prevent the small R134a molecules from passing through the hose (see Chapter 2), and to prevent moisture from passing through the hose into the system oil.

If you're likely to be working with basic, manual equipment, if possible buy hoses which are fitted with hand bleed valves at one end, or ideally at both ends (it should be possible to fit suitable valves yourself if none are fitted already). This will allow air to be easily bled from the hoses when carrying out work on an air conditioning system, preventing air from entering the system.

Units of pressure measurement

The pressure measured when working on an air conditioning system is usually expressed in pounds per square inch (psi) or kPa.

The readings shown on manifold gauge sets are known as gauge pressures because the readings obtained are affected by atmospheric pressure.

Correcting pressure gauge readings

Atmospheric pressure is the pressure exerted by the weight of the atmosphere on the earth's surface at any given point. Atmospheric pressure is 14.7 psi (absolute), or 101.4 kPa (absolute) at sea level, but this figure varies according to weather conditions (a negligible effect as far as air conditioning systems are concerned), and altitude. Atmospheric pressure reduces approximately 0.5 psi (3.45 kPa) for every 1000 feet (300 m) increase in altitude (although the reduction is not linear at high altitudes). From this, we can

see that even at an altitude of 10,000 feet (3000 m), the pressure correction, which has to be added to the gauge reading, is only 4.6 psi (31.7 kPa), which is barely significant (a typical figure for the low side system pressure under normal conditions is 30 psi/207 kPa). As it's very unlikely that work will be carried out on a vehicle air conditioning system at these high altitudes, in practise, we can forget about pressure corrections.

Units of vacuum measurement (low side gauge)

When checking and diagnosing air conditioning systems, vacuum is usually measured in inches of mercury (in Hg), or millimetres of mercury (mm Hg). Perfect vacuum is defined as 29.92 in Hg (760 mm Hg) at sea level with the atmospheric pressure at 14.7 psi (101.4 kPa).

The low side gauge on a manifold gauge set has a vacuum section, which reads in an anti-clockwise direction.

Correcting vacuum readings

The low side gauge will only measure vacuum accurately at sea level, and at high altitudes the gauge will read low. As with the pressure readings, a pressure correction has to be added to the gauge reading according to altitude (weather effects are negligible) to give an accurate reading. The figure for a perfect vacuum reduces approximately 1 in Hg (25.4 mm Hg) for every 1000 feet (300 m) increase in altitude (although the reduction is not linear at high altitudes).

In practice, this will be insignificant, as we rarely need to measure the actual value of vacuum in an air conditioning system, we only need to know whether or not vacuum is present.

Service adapter fittings for manifold gauges

Service adapters will be required for work on many types of system, usually to enable access to awkwardly located service connections **(see illustration)**. For example, it may be necessary to use a right-angle adapter in order to reach some connections, or it may be necessary to use a straight extension adapter. You may also find some R12 system vehicles with non-standard threads on the service connections, in which case suitable adapters will be required. Adapters are also available with short flexible extension hoses, and with anti-blow-back refrigerant check valves, which prevent refrigerant discharge when disconnecting high side service hoses.

A wide range of adapters is available, either individually or in sets, although it may be more cost-effective to buy items individually as you need them, rather than buying an expensive set of adapters, many of which you may never use.

Connecting a manifold gauge set to an air conditioning system

Refer to Chapter 6 for details.

4

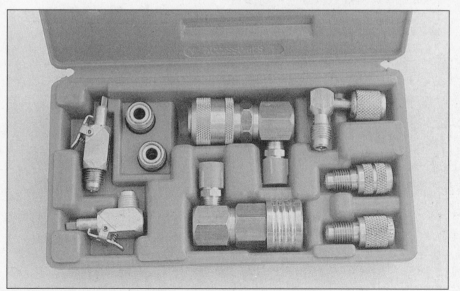

A typical set of service adapter fittings

Vacuum pump

If an air conditioning system has had the refrigerant discharged in order to carry out service or repair, or refrigerant has been lost due to a leak, or if there is any evidence of refrigerant contamination, the system must be evacuated to remove air and moisture, before it can be recharged with refrigerant.

Air and moisture must be removed from the system using a vacuum pump. A vacuum pump will draw air from the closed system to create a vacuum. By lowering the pressure inside the system to a vacuum, the boiling point of water, or moisture, is lowered to a point at which evaporation easily occurs. To remove all the moisture from the system, it's necessary to lower the boiling point of the water in the system to a point lower than the ambient air temperature (the temperature of the air surrounding the vehicle). The vaporised moisture is then easily drawn out by the vacuum pump.

To be sure of removing all the moisture from the system, the system must be evacuated as close as possible to a perfect vacuum (29.92 in Hg or 760 mm Hg at sea level). Although we've seen earlier that the figure for a perfect vacuum varies with altitude, the boiling point of water varies with altitude to a similar degree, so we can forget about corrections due to altitude when evacuating a system.

Types of vacuum pump

Two basic types of vacuum pump are available, the venturi-type, or the rotary vane-type. The rotary vane-type pump is generally more suited to automotive air conditioning work.

Venturi-type vacuum pump

The venturi-type vacuum pump is inexpensive and maintenance free; it has no

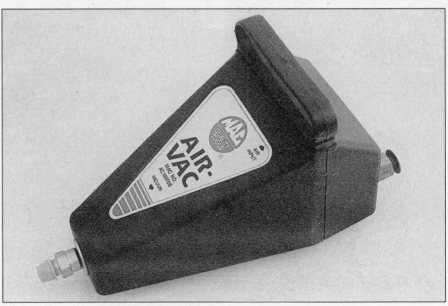

Venturi-type vacuum pump

moving parts, and requires no lubricating oil **(see illustration)**. This type of pump relies on a compressor to evacuate the system, and the compressor must pump around 80 to 90 psi (552 to 621 kPa). This can take a lot of power if an electric compressor is used.

Rotary vane-type vacuum pump

The rotary vane-type compressor consists of a small electric motor driving a pump **(see illustration)**. This type of pump is more expensive than a venturi-type, and also requires routine lubrication, but it is more efficient, and is generally more durable for frequent use.

Using a vacuum pump

Refer to Chapter 6 for details.

Rotary vane-type vacuum pump

Typical R134a refrigerant handling machine

Refrigerant recovery machine

Recovery machines are designed to remove refrigerant from an air conditioning system without polluting the environment. A wide range of recovery equipment is available from different manufacturers, and the equipment should always be used in accordance with the manufacturer's instructions. Unless the manufacturer specifies otherwise (some machines have separate circuits for R12 and R134a refrigerant), recovery machines and hoses used on R12 systems cannot be used on R134a systems, and *vice versa*, so separate sets of equipment will be required for R12 and R134a systems.

Some recovery machines are integrated into a refrigerant handling and processing machine which will allow system discharging, evacuation, refrigerant recycling (cleaning and removal of moisture), and recharging **(see illustration)**.

Refrigerant cylinders

Various types and sizes of refrigerant cylinders are available, and a number of cylinders may be required for handling fresh (virgin), reclaimable and waste refrigerant, according to the type of work to be carried out. Always use valved cylinders, with a safety pressure release valve.

Bulk refrigerant cylinders

Two basic types of bulk refrigerant cylinders are available, dual-port valved cylinders, and single-port valved cylinders, although not all suppliers provide both types **(see illustration)**. If you have the option of dual-port cylinders, and your budget allows, they are more convenient to use than single-port types, although single-port types are perfectly adequate.

Some air conditioning systems require charging with refrigerant vapour, whereas some require charging with refrigerant in a liquid state. A dual-port cylinder will allow vapour or liquid to be released from the cylinder depending on which of the two valves on the cylinder is opened (normally coded blue for vapour, and red for liquid). A single-port cylinder will also allow vapour or liquid to be released, but the cylinder must be standing upright if vapour is required, or inverted if liquid is required.

Obviously, R12 and R134a cylinders will be required if work is to be carried out on both systems.

Many refrigerant suppliers operate a cylinder delivery and collection service, and you may find that you have the option of leasing the cylinders, or purchasing them outright.

Although at present in the UK there are no restrictions on the purchase of refrigerant, it is likely that future legislation will require that anyone wishing to purchase refrigerant will have to be in possession of an appropriate refrigerant handler's certificate.

Typical R134a bulk refrigerant cylinder

1 Low pressure (vapour) refrigerant port
2 High pressure (liquid) refrigerant port
3 Overfill warning light switch (connected to a light on the refrigerant handling machine)

4

Waste refrigerant (reclaim) cylinders

A waste cylinder will be required to store waste refrigerant which cannot be recycled. Provided that the cylinder is only filled with waste refrigerant, ie, refrigerant which is known to be badly contaminated and will not be recycled, then one cylinder can be used for all waste refrigerant, regardless of type.

A single-port valved cylinder is perfectly adequate for storing waste refrigerant.

Recycling cylinders

Unless your refrigerant handling equipment has a built-in recycling cylinder (many do), recycling cylinders will be required to store refrigerant which has been removed from a system, and is to be cleaned, dried and recycled. Separate cylinders will be required for recycling R12 and R134a refrigerant; always ensure that the correct cylinder is used to avoid cross-contamination.

Dual-port valved cylinders and single-port valved cylinders are available, but you should check the recommendations supplied with your recycling equipment before deciding which type to obtain; some recycling equipment is designed for use with a dual-port cylinder.

Refrigerant comparator (slide rule type)

A refrigerant comparator can be used to identify the refrigerant in an air conditioning system before carrying out any work on the system (never assume that the correct refrigerant has been used – see Chapter 6). A comparator is a useful tool if you do not have access to an electronic refrigerant gas analyser.

A refrigerant comparator consists of a slide rule with a number of scales, and a vertical fixed line, which can be moved along the scales (see illustration). The top scale usually represents pressure (measured in psi or kPa), and there is an additional scale for each refrigerant type, representing refrigerant temperature.

A comparator can be used in conjunction with a manifold gauge set, and an accurate thermometer, to identify the type of refrigerant present in an air conditioning system. Details of how to use a comparator are given in Chapter 6, Identifying the refrigerant in the system.

Note that many manifold gauge sets have temperature scales incorporated into the gauges – this will give an indication as to the temperature to be expected for a particular refrigerant pressure.

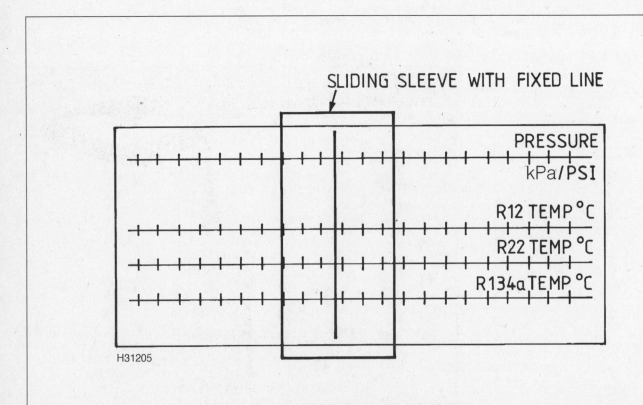

H31205

Typical refrigerant comparator

Accurate thermometer

An accurate thermometer is essential for carrying out servicing and fault diagnosis work on an air conditioning system. A thermometer which had a range from at least –4 to 52ºC (25 to 125ºF) will be required, and a –18 to 104ºC (0 to 220ºF) range will be even better.

Conventional thermometers are available in capillary tube and dial configurations, although dial types are easier to read and more versatile than traditional capillary tube types.

A wide range of digital thermometers is available. Digital thermometers are faster, more accurate, and easier to read. Many digital thermometers can be equipped with air, surface or immersion probes which makes them ideal for air conditioning work **(see illustration)**.

Leak detection equipment

A wide range of air conditioning system leak detection equipment is available, and sometimes several types of equipment may have to be used before a leak is finally located. Leakage, either through loose hose fittings, deteriorated hoses or seals, or damaged metal lines, is the most common cause of low refrigerant charge. The most commonly used leak detection equipment includes:

- *Bubble solution*
- *Electronic leak detection*
- *Tracer dye*
- *Halide torch (R12 only)*
- *Oxygen-free nitrogen (OFN) pressure testing equipment (described later in this Chapter)*

Let's take a look at the various equipment in more detail.

Bubble solution

This is an inexpensive way to find a leak, and can be used on a system which is charged with refrigerant (although, strictly speaking, the system should be discharged if an obvious leak is present – it's an offence to knowingly vent refrigerant to the atmosphere), or with oxygen-free nitrogen (OFN) pressure testing equipment on a system which has been discharged. Special coloured dye bubble spray solution is available to make any leaks easier to see.

The bubble solution (even soapy water solution can provide reasonable results) is applied to the area around the suspected leak with a small brush, or a spray. Any leaking refrigerant or OFN will cause the solution to form bubbles.

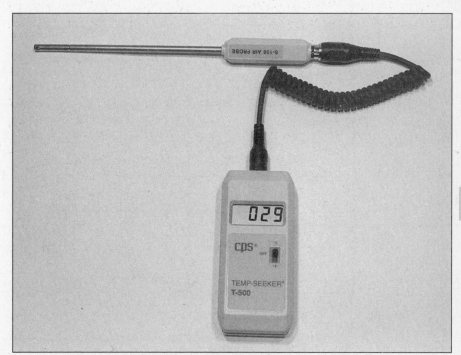

An accurate digital thermometer is invaluable for air conditioning work

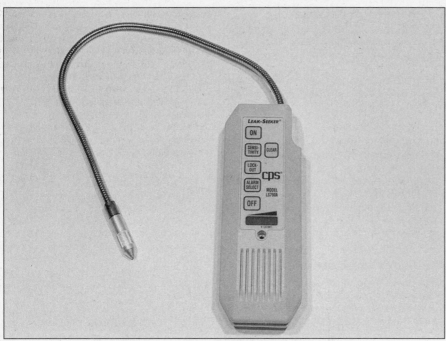

Typical reset guiding type electronic leak detector

Electronic leak detection

A number of different types of electronic leak detectors are available from different manufacturers. Some units are more sensitive than others, and several different methods of leak indication may be used. The most commonly used method of leak indication is an audible alarm-type warning.

One of the best types of electronic detector is the reset guiding-type **(see illustration)**. This type of machine allows the sensitivity to be reduced as desired, allowing the user to

'home-in' on the source of a leak. Once a leak has been detected, and the warning reaches a maximum, the sensitivity can be reduced, allowing the machine to be moved closer to the source of the leak before another leak indication is given. Other types of detector will detect a leak, but it can be difficult to locate the exact source due to the high sensitivity of the detector.

Note that some electronic leak detectors are sensitive to vehicle exhaust fumes, which can give false readings if a vehicle is running nearby.

Tracer dye

Tracer dye can be added to a system with the refrigerant when the system is charged. Some vehicle manufacturers add tracer dye when the systems are first filled at the factory. Tracer dyes are designed to be visible when exposed to ultra-violet light, so an ultra-violet light source will be required to use them **(see illustration)**.

Kits are available to allow tracer dye to be added to a system when recharging with refrigerant; this will aid leak detection, should a leak occur at a later date. Always check that the dye being used is compatible with the refrigerant and compressor oil used in the system – solvent-based dyes should **never** be used.

To find a leak using tracer dye, an ultra-violet light gun is shone at the various system components and refrigerant lines. A leak will show up as a brightly-coloured area around the source of the leak. Always use tracer dye equipment in accordance with the manufacturer's instructions.

 Warning: Always wear suitable eye protection when working with an ultra-violet light source.

Halide torch (R12 only)

The halide torch was once a common tool used for refrigerant leak detection. A halide torch uses a propane flame, which changes colour in the presence of R12 refrigerant (a halide torch will not detect R134a). This tool has one serious flaw, and that is that R12 refrigerant burns when exposed to a flame to produce deadly phosgene gas (mustard gas).

Although an experienced operator may decide to use a halide torch occasionally in order to identify whether a refrigerant is R12 or R134a (see Chapter 6, *Identifying the refrigerant in the system*), it is strongly recommended that a halide torch is **NEVER** used for leak detection.

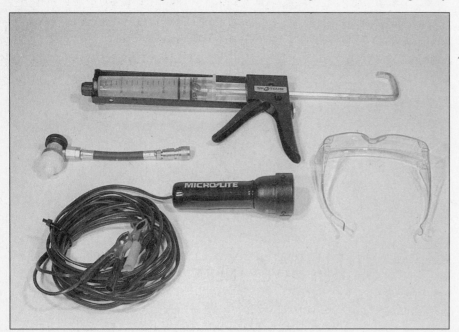

Tracer dye leak testing kit

Liquid refrigerant charging cylinder

A liquid refrigerant charging cylinder allows an air conditioning system to be charged with liquid refrigerant.

The charging cylinder is filled with liquid refrigerant from a bulk cylinder, and the charging cylinder is connected to the air conditioning system via a set of manifold gauges. The system is then charged from the cylinder. Using a charging cylinder allows the required quantity of liquid refrigerant to be delivered into the system.

Separate charging cylinders will be required for R12 and R134a refrigerant.

Charging cylinders incorporate a sight glass, a pressure gauge, and a rotating graduated sleeve (see illustration). These features allow compensation to be made for the fact that the volume of liquid refrigerant varies with temperature and pressure.

Liquid refrigerant charging is normally carried out with the air conditioning system switched off. The charging cylinder is heated, using a built-in heating element or an electric blanket type heater, to enable the refrigerant to flow from the charging cylinder into the system.

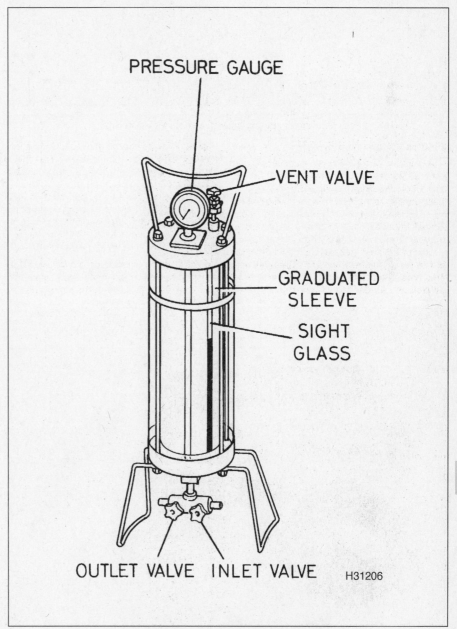

Typical liquid refrigerant charging cylinder

4

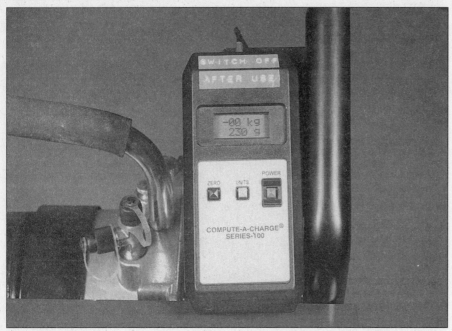

A set of scales with a digital readout which can be easily zeroed will simplify refrigerant vapour charging

Accurate scales

An accurate set of scales is essential to determine the quantity of refrigerant present in a bulk cylinder (and so to prevent overfilling of waste cylinders, etc). Scales will also be required when vapour charging an air conditioning system, to ensure that the correct quantity of refrigerant is added to the system.

An accurate set of bathroom scales can be used to give reasonable results, but ideally, an accurate set of digital scales which can be easily zeroed should be used **(see illustration)**.

Multimeter

A good quality multimeter is an essential tool for air conditioning fault diagnosis work **(see illustration)**. Any accurate multimeter capable of measuring suitable ranges of voltage, current and resistance can be used.

Compressor oil level dipsticks

Compressor oil level dipsticks will be required for checking the oil level on certain types of compressor with an oil sump. The type of dipstick required will vary according to the type of compressor fitted. It may be

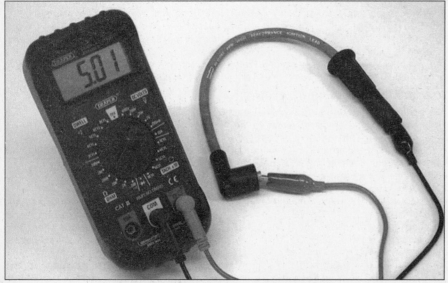

A good quality multimeter is an essential tool

possible to obtain dipsticks for some types of compressor, although if none are available it will be necessary to improvise (see Chapter 6, *Compressor oils*).

Compressor oil

A range of suitable compressor oils will be required in order to top up the oil when charging systems with refrigerant. Mineral oil will be required for R12 systems, and synthetic PAG oil will be required for R134a systems. Both types of oil come in a range of viscosities (although almost all R12 system compressors use the same grade of oil), and it's vital to ensure that the correct viscosity of oil is used (see Chapter 6, *Compressor oils*).

Oxygen-free nitrogen (OFN) pressure testing equipment

Oxygen-free nitrogen (OFN) equipment can be used for pressure testing air conditioning systems when searching for leaks (see Chapter 6, *Leak testing*). It is not a good idea to pressure test a system using refrigerant, because refrigerant will be released into the atmosphere (it's an offence to knowingly release refrigerant into the atmosphere). OFN is a safe, harmless gas, which can be vented to the atmosphere without any risk of damage to the environment.

In order to pressure-test an air conditioning system successfully, it may sometimes be necessary to use additional equipment in conjunction with OFN equipment, such as dye leak detection equipment.

The following OFN equipment is useful when carrying out work on a vehicle air conditioning system:
- *OFN cylinder*
- *Pressure regulator with 0 to 150 psi (0 to 1034 kPa) range*
- *Suitable connecting hoses for R12 and R134a service fittings*

OFN equipment can also be used for other servicing operations, eg, as a source of pressure for flushing air conditioning system components (air should **never** be pumped into a system), and even for operating tools which would normally run on compressed air.

Refrigerant recycling machine

A refrigerant recycling machine will allow refrigerant removed from a system to be recycled (provided that it is not excessively contaminated). Refrigerant should never be removed from one vehicle and used to charge another system without recycling, because of the risk of cross-contamination. Separate recycling equipment will be required for R12 and R134a systems.

Recycling machines are often integrated into refrigerant handling machines along with refrigerant recovery machines, vacuum pumps and charging equipment.

Although there are companies who provide a refrigerant recycling service, if a large amount of work is being done on air conditioning systems, it will probably prove more economical in the long run to purchase suitable recycling equipment.

Refrigerant cylinder heater

When transferring refrigerant from one container to another, or when charging an air conditioning system, it is often necessary to warm refrigerant containers. This can be done by placing the cylinder in a bath of hot (but not boiling) water, but a quicker and more effective method is to use an electric cylinder heater.

Heaters are available in the form of an electric belt which can be clipped in place around the cylinder and connected to a power source. Most heaters have a thermostat, which will turn the heater on and off as necessary once a predetermined maximum temperature has been reached.

 Warning: Never attempt to use a heat source with a naked flame to warm a refrigerant container.

Component flushing equipment

If a condenser, evaporator, or any of the system pipework is thought to be contaminated or blocked, the relevant component can be flushed to remove the obstruction(s).

Various manufacturers produce different types of flushing equipment. A special flushing fluid should be used, which will not cause component or refrigerant contamination and, ideally, flushing pressure should be provided by oxygen-free nitrogen (OFN), because this will avoid the introduction of air (and hence moisture) into the system. It's possible to use compressed air as an alternative to OFN, but obviously this will introduce air and moisture into the component(s) being flushed (it should be possible to remove all the air and moisture if the system is evacuated for an extended period).

Flushing is most easily carried out using a valved flushing cylinder filled with flushing fluid, connected between an OFN or air supply and the component to be flushed.

Compressor oil injector (for use when recharging with refrigerant)

A compressor oil injector can be used to add compressor oil when recharging a system with refrigerant.

A measured quantity of oil is added to the injector, and the injector is connected in the refrigerant recharging line, between the refrigerant container and the manifold gauge set.

Separate injectors will be required for mineral oil (R12 systems) and PAG oil (R134a systems).

4

Electronic refrigerant gas analyser

Electronic refrigerant gas analysers are expensive, but allow quick and reliable identification of refrigerants, eliminating the need for analysis using a manifold gauge set, thermometer and comparator **(see illustration)**.

To use an electronic analyser, a vapour (not liquid) sample is usually required. Most analysers will give a read-out of the percentage composition of the vapour, and will indicate whether the refrigerant is suitable for recycling. Some analysers allow a print-out of the analysis to be generated, which can provide a useful record of the findings for a particular vehicle.

Spring-lock coupling release tool kit

A set of release tools will be required in order to disconnect the spring-lock refrigerant line connections found on some vehicles (particularly Fords). Details of how to use the release tools are given in *Basic repair procedures* in Chapter 6.

Orifice tube removal tool

A special removal tool will be required in order to remove an orifice tube from the evaporator inlet pipe. The tool engages with lugs on the orifice tube, and the nut on the top of the tool is then turned to pull the orifice tube from the pipe. Refer to *Orifice tube renewal* in Chapter 6 for details.

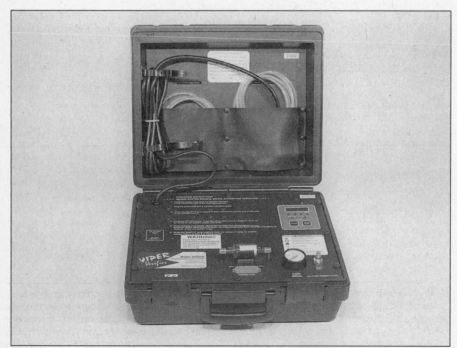

Portable electronic refrigerant gas analyser

Chapter 5
Safety

Contents

Introduction .... 5•1
General safety .... 5•2
  General hazards .... 5•2
  Special hazards .... 5•2

Air conditioning system safety precautions .... 5•3
  The hazards .... 5•3
  Safety clothing .... 5•3
  Do's and Don'ts .... 5•3

5

Introduction

Whenever any work is carried out on a vehicle, safety must always be the first consideration. In addition to the usual precautions which must be taken when working on any vehicle, air conditioning systems present a range of additional hazards.

It is strongly suggested that the contents of this Chapter are read thoroughly and understood before attempting any of the work described in Chapter 6.

Note: *Although this book contains comprehensive information on air conditioning service procedures, repairs and trouble-shooting, it is strongly recommended that anyone intending to carry out work on an air conditioning system for the first time attends a recognised automotive air conditioning training course, which includes some practical work. Air conditioning work is not a task for the DIY mechanic – any mistakes made can be costly, both in terms of safety and financially.*

General safety

Working on your car can be dangerous. This page shows just some of the potential risks and hazards, with the aim of creating a safety-conscious attitude.

General hazards

Scalding

• Don't remove the radiator or expansion tank cap while the engine is hot.
• Engine oil, automatic transmission fluid or power steering fluid may also be dangerously hot if the engine has recently been running.

Burning

• Beware of burns from the exhaust system and from any part of the engine. Brake discs and drums can also be extremely hot immediately after use.

Crushing

• When working under or near a raised vehicle, always supplement the jack with axle stands, or use drive-on ramps. *Never venture under a car which is only supported by a jack.*
• Take care if loosening or tightening high-torque nuts when the vehicle is on stands. Initial loosening and final tightening should be done with the wheels on the ground.

Fire

• Fuel is highly flammable; fuel vapour is explosive.
• Don't let fuel spill onto a hot engine.
• Do not smoke or allow naked lights (including pilot lights) anywhere near a vehicle being worked on. Also beware of creating sparks (electrically or by use of tools).
• Fuel vapour is heavier than air, so don't work on the fuel system with the vehicle over an inspection pit.
• Another cause of fire is an electrical overload or short-circuit. Take care when repairing or modifying the vehicle wiring.
• Keep a fire extinguisher handy, of a type suitable for use on fuel and electrical fires.

Electric shock

• Ignition HT voltage can be dangerous, especially to people with heart problems or a pacemaker. Don't work on or near the ignition system with the engine running or the ignition switched on.

• Mains voltage is also dangerous. Make sure that any mains-operated equipment is correctly earthed. Mains power points should be protected by a residual current device (RCD) circuit breaker.

Fume or gas intoxication

• Exhaust fumes are poisonous; they often contain carbon monoxide, which is rapidly fatal if inhaled. Never run the engine in a confined space such as a garage with the doors shut.
• Fuel vapour is also poisonous, as are the vapours from some cleaning solvents and paint thinners.

Poisonous or irritant substances

• Avoid skin contact with battery acid and with any fuel, fluid or lubricant, especially antifreeze, brake hydraulic fluid and Diesel fuel. Don't syphon them by mouth. If such a substance is swallowed or gets into the eyes, seek medical advice.
• Prolonged contact with used engine oil can cause skin cancer. Wear gloves or use a barrier cream if necessary. Change out of oil-soaked clothes and do not keep oily rags in your pocket.
• Air conditioning refrigerant forms a poisonous gas if exposed to a naked flame (including a cigarette). It can also cause skin burns on contact.

Asbestos

• Asbestos dust can cause cancer if inhaled or swallowed. Asbestos may be found in gaskets and in brake and clutch linings. When dealing with such components it is safest to assume that they contain asbestos.

Special hazards

Hydrofluoric acid

• This extremely corrosive acid is formed when certain types of synthetic rubber, found in some O-rings, oil seals, fuel hoses etc, are exposed to temperatures above 4000ºC. The rubber changes into a charred or sticky substance containing the acid. Once formed,

the acid remains dangerous for years. If it gets onto the skin, it may be necessary to amputate the limb concerned.
• When dealing with a vehicle which has suffered a fire, or with components salvaged from such a vehicle, wear protective gloves and discard them after use.

The battery

• Batteries contain sulphuric acid, which attacks clothing, eyes and skin. Take care when topping-up or carrying the battery.
• The hydrogen gas given off by the battery is highly explosive. Never cause a spark or allow a naked light nearby. Be careful when connecting and disconnecting battery chargers or jump leads.

Air bags

• Air bags can cause injury if they go off accidentally. Take care when removing the steering wheel and/or facia. Special storage instructions may apply.

Diesel injection equipment

• Diesel injection pumps supply fuel at very high pressure. Take care when working on the fuel injectors and fuel pipes.

Warning: Never expose the hands, face or any other part of the body to injector spray; the fuel can penetrate the skin with potentially fatal results.

Remember...

DO

• Do use eye protection when using power tools, and when working under the vehicle.
• Do wear gloves or use barrier cream to protect your hands when necessary.
• Do get someone to check periodically that all is well when working alone on the vehicle.
• Do keep loose clothing and long hair well out of the way of moving mechanical parts.
• Do remove rings, wristwatch etc, before working on the vehicle – especially the electrical system.
• Do ensure that any lifting or jacking equipment has a safe working load rating adequate for the job.

DON'T

• Don't attempt to lift a heavy component which may be beyond your capability – get assistance.
• Don't rush to finish a job, or take unverified short cuts.
• Don't use ill-fitting tools which may slip and cause injury.
• Don't leave tools or parts lying around where someone can trip over them. Mop up oil and fuel spills at once.
• Don't allow children or pets to play in or near a vehicle being worked on.

Air conditioning system safety precautions

The hazards

When working with air conditioning systems, there are certain specific hazards, which require special precautions to be taken.

• **Refrigerant**. Firstly, refrigerant evaporates rapidly when exposed to the atmosphere, causing it to freeze anything it contacts; this can cause severe frostbite and cold burns. Secondly, refrigerant forms a highly poisonous gas when exposed to an open flame; R12 forms phosgene (mustard) gas, and R134a forms hydrogen fluoride, both of which are deadly if inhaled. Additionally, refrigerant is poisonous in large quantities, and is heavier than air, which can cause hazards when working in an enclosed environment.

• **System pressure**. The high side of an air conditioning system is under very high pressure, which will result in a high pressure penetrating jet of refrigerant if a leak occurs. This could cause severe injury to eyes and skin.

• **Compressor oils**. The synthetic PAG oil used in R134a systems is poisonous, and extremely hygroscopic. It is easily absorbed through the skin, and will rapidly absorb moisture from the skin. Always wear non-absorbent gloves, and handle compressor oils with care.

Safety clothing

• **Always wear non-absorbent gloves, and eye protection**, when carrying out any work on an air conditioning system (including connecting and disconnecting service equipment), or when handling refrigerants or compressor oils.

• **Always wear overalls or a protective coat, and don't work with bare arms**. Don't be tempted to work with rolled-up sleeves, even on a hot day.

• **Wear safety shoes or boots** when handling refrigerant cylinders. Refrigerant cylinders are heavy, and toes are fragile!

Do's and Don'ts

Do

• Do wear non-absorbent gloves and eye protection at all times when working on an air conditioning system.

• Do keep loose clothing and long hair clear of the condenser cooling fan(s).

• Do ensure adequate ventilation when working in an enclosed space.

• Do ensure that anyone working in the vicinity is aware of the hazards present when work is being carried out on an air conditioning system. (No smoking, no naked flames, no welding, no working in inspection pits, etc.)

• Do fit protective valve caps to system service connections and refrigerant container valves when not in use.

• Do store refrigerant containers in a cool place, away from direct sources of heat and naked flames.

• Do use an exhaust extractor when running an engine in an enclosed space. In addition to the usual exhaust fumes hazard, leaking refrigerant can be burnt inside the engine to produce poisonous gas at the exhaust.

• Do discharge the air conditioning system before placing the vehicle inside a paint curing oven. The high temperatures can cause extremely high pressures (300+ psi/2069+ kPa) in the system which could cause seals and connections to leak, or hoses to burst.

• Do discharge the air conditioning system before carrying out any welding work near system components.

• Do counterhold refrigerant line connections when slackening threaded fittings, to avoid twisting the refrigerant lines.

• Do refit caps to compressor oil containers immediately after use.

Don't

• Don't smoke when working on or near a vehicle air conditioning system.

• Don't use a space heater when working on an air conditioning system in an enclosed space.

• Don't carry out welding work near air conditioning system components when the system is charged.

• Don't vent refrigerant into the atmosphere.

• Don't try to stop refrigerant escaping if a major leak occurs whilst working on a system, move clear immediately until the leak stops.

• Don't operate an air conditioning system without first verifying that all connections, particularly those to service equipment, are tight and secure.

• Don't carry out any work on an air conditioning system using an inspection pit.

• Don't store refrigerant containers close to a heat source, or outside in direct sunlight.

• Don't hit or strike refrigerant lines or heat exchangers on a charged air conditioning system. A blow could easily cause the soft metal to rupture.

5

Chapter 6
Service and repair procedures

Contents

Introduction . . . . .6•1
Air conditioning system do's and don'ts . . . . .6•2
Service valves . . . . .6•3
   Types of service valve . . . . .6•4
   R12 and R134a service valves . . . . .6•6
Regular servicing . . . . .6•7
   Annual system check . . . . .6•7
Basic service procedures . . . . .6•8
   Preliminary work . . . . .6•8
   Compressor oils . . . . .6•17
   Discharging a system . . . . .6•20

Pressure testing a system . . . . .6•22
Evacuating a system . . . . .6•23
Filling a container with refrigerant . . . . .6•24
Charging a system with refrigerant .6•25
Leak testing . . . . .6•28
Flushing system components . . . . .6•29
Basic repair procedures . . . . .6•30
   Refrigerant line connections . . . . .6•30
   Curing leaks . . . . .6•31
   Component renewal . . . . .6•32
   Compressor overhaul . . . . .6•34

Introduction

The previous Chapters have dealt with the basic principles of air conditioning system operation, and details of the individual components which make up a typical system. We've also looked at the tools and equipment required to work on an air conditioning system, so now let's take a look at the various procedures necessary to service and repair an air conditioning system.

Whether you're discharging a system in order to allow other work to be carried out on a vehicle (eg, engine removal on some vehicles, or vehicle respraying work involving a paint curing oven) or carrying out fault

diagnosis work on the air conditioning system itself, there is a definite sequence of work which should always be followed. These procedures should always be performed properly and safely, and there is no room for short-cuts.

Note that most integrated refrigerant handling machines will perform all the basic service operations described in this Chapter (discharging, evacuation and recharging), and incorporate equipment such a manifold gauge set, scales and vacuum pump in a single unit. The procedures described in this Chapter assume that basic equipment is being used. If

an integrated refrigerant handling machine is being used, the same basic principles apply, but always follow the equipment manufacturer's instructions.

It is strongly recommended that anyone intending to carry out work on an air conditioning system for the first time attends a recognised automotive air conditioning training course, which includes some practical work. Air conditioning work is not a task for the DIY mechanic – any mistakes made can be costly, both in terms of safety and financially.

6

Air conditioning system do's and don'ts

In addition to the safety precautions given in Chapter 5, when working on an air conditioning system there are certain other fundamental precautions to take in order to maintain the efficiency of the system and to avoid damage to the system components.

Do's

• Do check that sufficient compressor oil has been added to the system whenever any refrigerant discharging or recharging work is carried out.
• Do check that the condenser cooling fan(s) turn freely before carrying out any work on the system. A seized condenser fan can lead to rapid overheating of the condenser and excessive system pressures.
• Do test to see what type of refrigerant is in the system before carrying out any work. Never assume that the correct refrigerant has been used in the system.
• Do discharge a system before attempting to open any refrigerant lines, or carrying out any work on the system components.
• Do use separate sets of equipment for working with R12 and R134a systems. Refrigerant cross-contamination can cause serious problems.
• Do use only the refrigerant type specified by the vehicle manufacturer (ie, R12 or R134a, according to recommendations) when charging a system. The use of any other types of refrigerant may invalidate the vehicle warranty, and may cause problems with the system components, and/or system contamination problems.
• Do carry out a leak test on a system before charging with refrigerant.
• Do ensure that all open pipework and component connections are covered or plugged immediately after disconnection. This is necessary to prevent contamination, and on R134a systems to prevent the compressor oil left in the system absorbing moisture.
• Do check that the service valves are not leaking before and after charging a system.
• Do dispose of waste refrigerant via a registered waste refrigerant handler.

Don'ts

• Don't deliberately vent refrigerant into the atmosphere.
• Don't fill an R12 system with R134a, and *vice versa*.
• Don't pressure test a system using air.
• Don't flush system components using anything other than solvents approved for air conditioning system work (NEVER flush using water).
• Don't run a system unless you're sure that it's charged with refrigerant.
• Don't run a system using any fluid other than refrigerant, including oxygen-free nitrogen (OFN).
• Don't allow service hoses to rest against the vehicle paintwork.

Typical low side service valve on a vehicle air conditioning system

Service valves

The service valves act as the 'doors' into a vehicle air conditioning system. Without service valves, it would be impossible to work on the system. All checking, fault diagnosis, discharging and charging procedures are performed through the service valves.

Most systems have at least two service valves, one on the low side of the system, and one on the high side of the system (see illustrations). Some systems may have more than one valve on the high and/or low side of the system to enable work to be carried out at different locations in the system. A few vehicles (eg, certain Audis) have only one valve on the low side of the system (the system must be discharged, and a special adapter must be fitted to the compressor to allow both the high and low sides of the system to be accessed).

There are no standard locations for service valves, and they could be found anywhere in the system. Although most service valves are found at accessible service points in metal refrigerant pipes, or on the compressor, on some vehicles one or both of the valves may be cunningly hidden (for example behind the headlight on certain Ford Galaxy models).

All service valves have protective caps, which keep them clean, and prevent accidental opening of the valves. The caps must be removed before any service hoses can be connected to the valves. Always replace any missing valve caps.

 Warning: Always remove service valve caps slowly; if a valve is leaking, this will prevent the cap from being blown off.

Typical high side service valve on a vehicle air conditioning system

6

Types of service valve

All modern vehicles are equipped with Schrader-type service valves which are self-sealing, and open and close automatically when a connection is made to them. A few, mainly older, vehicles (particularly US imports) may be fitted with manually-operated stem-type valves, but this is unusual.

Schrader valves

A Schrader-type service valve is basically the same in design and operation as a tyre valve. The valve has a spring-loaded mechanism which is normally in a closed position (when no service hoses are attached to it), preventing the escape of refrigerant from the system. When a service hose is connected to the valve, the valve stem is pushed down to the open position, and fluid can now flow from the system to the service hose or *vice versa* (see illustration).

⚠️ *Warning: If a system is charged with refrigerant, NEVER attach a hose or adapter to a Schrader service valve if the other end of the hose is open to the atmosphere. Always ensure that the hose is connected correctly to the service equipment first, then connect to the valve. Failure to observe this could result in the total loss of refrigerant from the system to the atmosphere at best, and personal injury at worst.*

It's important to note that although the Schrader service valve is similar in operation and appearance to a tyre valve, a service valve cannot be replaced with a tyre valve.

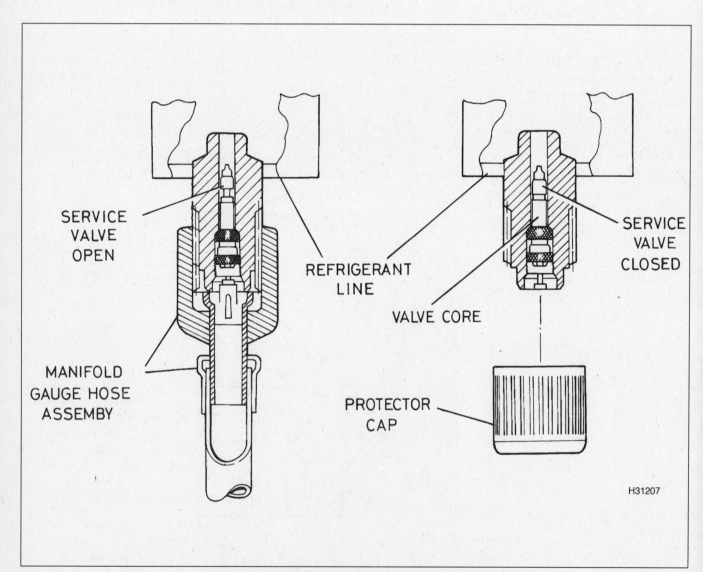

Schematic view of Schrader-type service valve operation

Manually-operated stem-type valves

This type of valve is much rarer than the Schrader-type, but stem-type valves may be encountered on older vehicles, and some later Mercedes vehicles.

The stem-type valve features a three-way connector, with an adjustable stem under a protective cap. When connecting the valve to a service hose, the valve stem must be manually positioned, using a special spanner to prevent damage. The valve has three positions:

a) *Back-seated (open) position.*
b) *Mid (test) position.*
c) *Front-seated (closed) position.*

The **back-seated position** of the valve is the normal operating position **(see illustration)**. This position blocks the passageway to the service port, preventing the flow of refrigerant to the port. This is the position the valve should be in when connecting or disconnecting a service hose.

The **mid (test) position** of the valve allows refrigerant to flow through the system and to the service port **(see illustration)**. This is the position the valve should be in once the service hose has been securely connected, in order to carry out any servicing work. The valve stem must be turned 1 to 2 turns clockwise from the back-seated position to reach the mid (test) position.

The **front-seated (closed) position** of the valve blocks refrigerant flow through the system **(see illustration)**. If the valve is located on the compressor (which it usually is), the flow of refrigerant from or to the compressor is blocked.

⚠ *Warning: If the air conditioning system is operated with the service valve(s) in the front-seated (closed) position, the compressor will be damaged.*

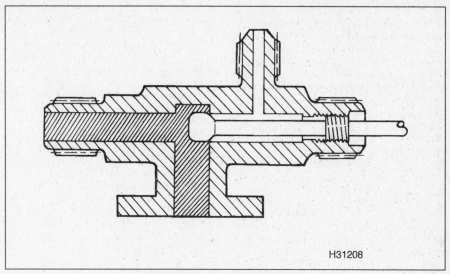

Stem-type service valve in back-seated position

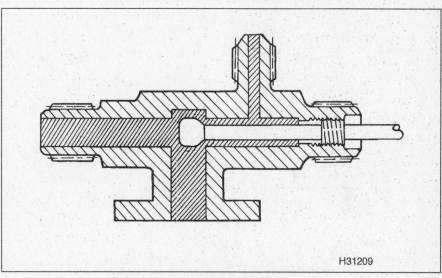

Stem-type service valve in mid (test) position

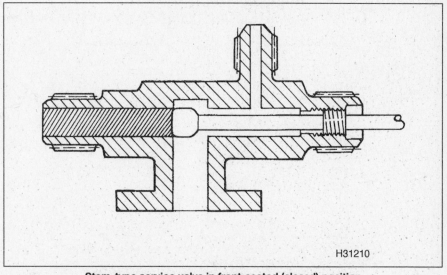

Stem-type service valve in front-seated (closed) position

6

R12 and R134a service valves

R12 and R134a system service valves have different connector types so that, in theory, it's impossible to connect R134a service equipment to an R12 system and *vice versa*.

⚠️ *Warning: Some vehicles eg, some Ford, Peugeot and Volvo models) may have a system which is fitted with R12 service valves, but is actually charged with R134a. Some vehicles may also be encountered which have R12 systems which have been retrofitted to use R134a. Normally, these systems will have a prominent label or plate fitted under the bonnet or on the compressor to indicate that they are filled with R134a. If there is any doubt as to the refrigerant in the system, identify the refrigerant (see Identifying the refrigerant in the system) before carrying out any discharging or charging work.*

R12 system valves

R12 system service valves have an external thread, which requires service hose connections to be screwed into place **(see illustration)**. Almost all modern vehicles have valves with standardised threads, although a few manufacturers use their own thread size, in which case suitable adapters will be required to enable service hoses to be connected.

On later vehicle fitted with R12 systems, the high and low side service valves have different sized connectors which prevents the high and low side connections to service equipment being accidentally reversed.

If work is being carried out on a system where the high and low side service valves have similar size connectors, great care should be taken to make sure that service equipment is connected correctly. If high and low side connections are reversed, serious damage to the system and service equipment and/or personal injury could result (due to the high pressures in the high side of the system). If any doubt exists about the identification of the high and low side service valves, check the location of the valves, and note the following (see Chapter 3):

• The **high side** runs from the outlet (or discharge) side of the compressor (often marked D), through the condenser and, where applicable, the filter/drier, to the expansion valve or orifice tube (as applicable).

• The **low side** is the remaining half of the system, from the expansion valve or orifice tube, through the evaporator and accumulator (where applicable) to the inlet (or suction) side of the compressor (often marked S).

If there is still any doubt as to the identification of the service valves, always connect the high pressure service hose first. This will prevent the possibility of damage to the gauges or equipment (if the low pressure gauge is connected to the high side of the system, the gauge could be irreparably damaged).

R134a system valves

R134a system service valves use 'snap-on' couplings, and have no external threads (the internal threads are for the valve caps only) **(see illustration)**. All vehicles use standard R134a service valves, and the high and low side service valves have different size connectors, which prevents high and low side service hoses from being connected incorrectly.

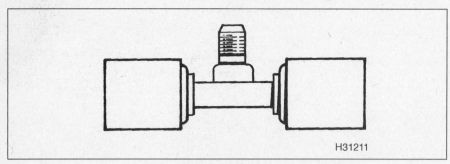

H31211

R12 service valve

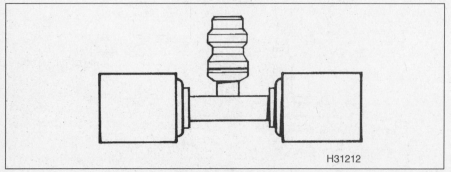

H31212

R134a service valve

Regular servicing

A vehicle air conditioning system requires regular servicing to ensure that it continues to operate efficiently. This is often overlooked, and many systems only receive attention when a problem occurs. Ideally, a vehicle air conditioning system should be serviced annually.

One of the simplest and most beneficial maintenance tasks is to switch on the air conditioning system and run it for five to ten minutes every month, regardless of the weather. This will ensure that the compressor oil is distributed evenly around the system, and will prevent the system seals from drying out. Compressor shaft seal failure is a common problem if the system is left for a long time without being run (this happens because the seal dries out, sticks to the compressor shaft, and rotates with the shaft when the compressor starts). If the compressor shaft seal fails, both refrigerant and compressor oil will be lost from the system.

As with any vehicle system, regular checking will enable any problems to be spotted and diagnosed before they cause major trouble **(see illustration)**.

An average R12 air conditioning system in good condition will lose between 25 and 100 g of refrigerant per year through porosity of components and minor leaks. This means that if the system is left for even a couple of years without checking, the refrigerant charge can become significantly lower than specified,

which will obviously have an effect on the efficiency of the system.

Over a period of time, particularly in the summer months, it's likely that the condenser fins will become covered with a layer of debris and dead insects. If this is allowed to build up, it will reduce the airflow through the condenser and the engine cooling system radiator, and will cause overheating. Regular checking will prevent any trouble.

Another source of trouble on a system which has had no maintenance is a blocked evaporator drain tube. If the drain tube is blocked, condensation from the evaporator will not be able to escape, and will build up in the evaporator casing. This will reduce the dehumidifying ability of the air conditioning system, and may cause unpleasant smells due to a build-up of bacteria in the evaporator casing.

Apart from checking on the problem areas already mentioned, ideally, an annual check of the system will allow for the system to be discharged, leak-tested, evacuated, and refilled with the correct quantity of refrigerant and compressor oil.

Annual system check

If possible, the following system checks should be carried out once a year. Although discharging and re-charging the system annually may at first sound like an unnecessary operation, it is the only way to be

sure that the system contains the correct quantity of uncontaminated refrigerant.

Although individual technicians may tailor the service schedule to their own requirements and, where applicable, to those of the customer, the following schedule lists all the operations which it is suggested are carried out annually.

• Check and if necessary clean the evaporator drain.
• Check and if necessary clean the condenser (brush loose debris from the fins, and if necessary clean the condenser using a hosepipe from the rear – never use compressed air, which can damage the cooling fins).
• Check the operation of the condenser cooling fan(s).
• Check the operation of the system, and the system temperatures and pressures.
• Check the system for leaks.
• Discharge the system, checking the moisture content of the refrigerant drawn out of the system.
• If excessive moisture was present in the refrigerant drawn out of the system, renew the desiccant in the filter/drier or accumulator (where applicable), or fit a new filter/drier or accumulator.
• Pressure test the system for leaks, then evacuate the system and recharge using the specified quantity of refrigerant and compressor oil.

Regular checking of an air conditioning system will help to prevent problems

6

Checking a compressor drivebelt tension

Check the coolant level

Basic service procedures

Preliminary work

⚠ *Warning: When working on an air conditioning system, the first priority must always be safety. Make sure that you have read the advice and precautions given in Chapter 5 before proceeding.*

Servicing an air conditioning system is not a difficult task, provided that you have access to the appropriate special equipment (see Chapter 4). Never attempt to improvise tools or refrigerant handling equipment.

Following a logical sequence of work will help to avoid any problems, which if overlooked, could cause confusion and problems later on.

Before carrying out any work on the system, it's good practise to carry out the following operations:

1) Check that the condenser fan works.
2) Carry out preliminary visual checks of the system components.
3) Connect a manifold (test) gauge set.
4) Stabilise the system.
5) Check the system temperatures and pressures.
6) Check the performance of the system.
7) Check for leaks.
8) Identify any refrigerant in the system.

We'll look at these operations in more detail before proceeding further.

Checking that the condenser fan works

To operate effectively, an air conditioning system requires a constant flow of cool air through the condenser. On a vehicle air conditioning system, the condenser is mounted in front of the engine cooling system radiator. When the air conditioning system is switched on, the cool air passing through the vehicle's front grille passes through the air conditioning system condenser, and absorbs heat, which means that the air is already warm when it reaches the cooling system radiator. This can easily lead to engine overheating, and excessive condenser temperatures (which will in turn lead to excessive air conditioning system high side pressure), especially when the vehicle is standing still.

To prevent overheating problems, a condenser/radiator cooling fan (sometimes more than one fan) is fitted, and on many vehicles fitted with air conditioning, the cooling fan will operate constantly whenever the air conditioning system is switched on.

How to check the condenser fan

⚠ *Warning: Take care when working around a cooling fan on a vehicle with a warm engine. On many vehicles fitted with an electric cooling fan, the fan may start even when the ignition is switched off.*

On a belt-driven fan, check that the drivebelt is in good condition and correctly tensioned **(see illustration)**.

On an electric fan, first of all check that the cooling fan blades are free to turn by spinning them by hand. If the blades are seized, fix the problem before carrying out any further work.

The fan is usually controlled using signals provided by an engine coolant temperature sensor, and by signals from a pressure or temperature sensor fitted in the air conditioning system. The operation of the cooling fan can be checked by disconnecting the motor wiring plug, and connecting the fan motor directly to a 12-volt power supply – take great care not to short out the power supply wire. If the fan fails to operate, the fan motor is almost certainly at fault.

Testing of the fan motor control circuit is usually possible, but the procedure will depend on the type of sensors and control system fitted. Be wary of using conventional test equipment if the fan is controlled by an engine management system electronic control unit (ECU), as the ECU may be damaged if the correct procedure is not followed.

Preliminary visual checks

Before carrying out any work on an air conditioning system, it's advisable to carry out a few visual checks to ensure that there are no fundamental problems with the system components.

1) Check the condition of the engine cooling system. Check for leaks, and make sure that the coolant level is correct **(see illustration)**.
2) Check that the air conditioning compressor drivebelt and, where applicable, the cooling fan drivebelt, is in good condition and correctly tensioned.
3) Check the operation of the cooling fan(s), as described previously.
4) Check that the condenser fins are not bent, damaged or clogged. If necessary, clean debris and insects from the fins using a soft brush.
5) Check for any obvious signs of refrigerant or compressor oil leaks. Look for staining on the refrigerant lines and the system components, particularly the condenser.

Checking the refrigerant condition using a sight glass (expansion valve systems)

Some expansion valve type systems which use R12 refrigerant have a refrigerant sight glass which allows the refrigerant in the system to be viewed. The sight glass is usually incorporated into the filter/drier assembly, ie, in the high pressure liquid refrigerant line. The sight glass relies on the fact that bubbles will form in the refrigerant when the refrigerant charge is low, and on the fact that the compressor oil is not usually visible when the refrigerant is circulating normally.

There are a few important points to make about sight glasses:

a) *A sight glass cannot be used on an orifice tube system because bubbles are always present in the refrigerant high pressure liquid line, even when the system is operating normally.*

b) *A sight glass cannot be used on an air conditioning system which uses R134a refrigerant because the synthetic compressor oil mixes with the refrigerant to give the liquid a milky appearance. This means that a sight glass will not give an accurate indication as to the condition of the refrigerant.*

c) *To use a sight glass, the air conditioning system must be operating.*

d) *Although it can be used as a visual indicator, if the sight glass suggests that there may be a problem, further testing should always be carried out to confirm or eliminate the problem. **A sight glass does not give a definitive indication as to the condition of the refrigerant.***

To use a sight glass, start the vehicle engine and switch on the air conditioning system, then wait for a few minutes for the system to stabilise. There are several conditions which may be indicated in a sight glass (**see illustration**):

❏ **Clear sight glass**. A clear sight glass can be good or bad news. It indicates one of three possibilities:

a) *The system has the correct refrigerant charge.*

b) *The system has no refrigerant in it. If this is true, the air conditioning system will provide no cool air through the heater/ventilation vents inside the vehicle.*

c) *The system is overcharged (too much refrigerant). This condition can only be verified by using a manifold (test) gauge set – see Connecting a manifold (test) gauge set.*

❏ **Occasional bubbles or foam in sight glass**. An occasionally bubbly or foamy sight glass indicates that the system is slightly low on refrigerant and air has probably entered the system. If the bubbles are sporadic (usually appearing during compressor clutch cycling or system start-up), their presence may not indicate a problem.

❏ **Heavy stream of bubbles**. A heavy stream of bubbles may indicate a very low refrigerant charge.

❏ **Oil streaks in sight glass**. Oil streaks may indicate that the system refrigerant charge is very low.

❏ **Dark or cloudy sight glass**. A dark or cloudy sight glass may indicate that the desiccant in the filter/drier has deteriorated and is being circulated through the system. It may also indicate that contaminants are present in the system.

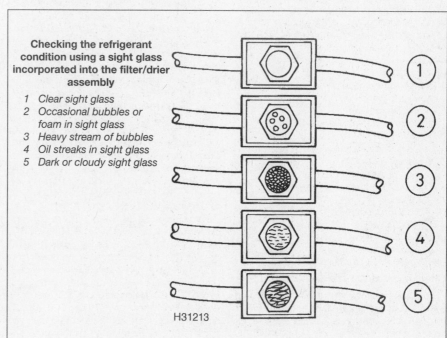

Checking the refrigerant condition using a sight glass incorporated into the filter/drier assembly

1 *Clear sight glass*
2 *Occasional bubbles or foam in sight glass*
3 *Heavy stream of bubbles*
4 *Oil streaks in sight glass*
5 *Dark or cloudy sight glass*

H31213

6

Connect the high side manifold gauge hose to the service valve on the high side of the system

Connecting a manifold (test) gauge set

Connecting a manifold gauge set (refer to Chapter 4 for further details) is a simple operation, but there are pitfalls for the unwary if the correct procedure is not followed:

1 First of all, locate the service connections on the vehicle and, where applicable, remove the valve covers from the connections.

⚠️ *Warning: Always wear goggles and non-absorbent gloves when removing valve caps, in case the Schrader valves are leaking. A leaking valve can cause the valve cap to fly off as it is unscrewed.*

2 Ensure that **both** manifold hand valves are **fully closed**.

3 Connect the low side hose (blue) to the service connection on the low side of the system, then connect the high side hose (red) to the service connection on the high side of the system **(see illustration)**. R12 connections are a screw-fit, whilst R134a connections are a snap-fit. Note that on most systems, the high side and low side connections are different sizes, so it shouldn't be possible to connect the hoses incorrectly.

4 The high and low side gauge hoses must now be purged of air. This should be done in accordance with the equipment manufacturer's instructions. Note that it may not be necessary to purge air from the hoses when using some integrated refrigerant handling equipment (the hoses may be self-purging – refer to the equipment manufacturer's instructions).

5 If necessary, the service (yellow) hose can be connected to a vacuum pump, refrigerant recovery machine, or refrigerant supply, depending on what type of work is to be carried out on the system **(see illustration)**.

6 Make sure that the gauge hoses are positioned clear of all moving and/or hot components in the engine compartment, and clear of the vehicle paintwork (which can be damaged due to the vibration of the hoses).

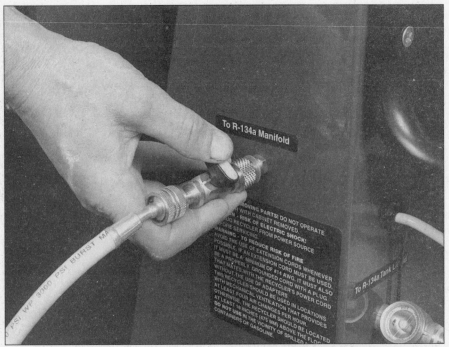

Connecting a manifold gauge service hose to a refrigerant handling machine

7 Where applicable, screw down the hand valves on the service valve ends of the gauge hoses, to open the Schrader valves. This will allow refrigerant pressure to reach the manifold gauges. Note that with the air conditioning system switched off, the pressures indicated on the high and low side gauges should be approximately equal **(see illustration)**.

⚠️ *Warning: DO NOT OPEN EITHER OF THE MANIFOLD GAUGE HAND VALVES WHEN THE SERVICE HOSE IS NOT CONNECTED TO ANYTHING. Refrigerant will be vented to the atmosphere.*

⚠️ *Warning: NEVER OPEN THE MANIFOLD GAUGE HIGH SIDE HAND VALVE WHILE THE AIR CONDITIONING SYSTEM IS OPERATING. High pressure refrigerant will force its way through the high side of the manifold test gauge and into the service hose. If the service hose is not connected to anything, this will vent high pressure refrigerant into the atmosphere. If the service hose is connected to a refrigerant cylinder, the pressure can be high enough to burst the cylinder safety valve fitting, or even rupture the cylinder, resulting in possible damage and injury.*

Note: *It is good practice to check the system service valves for leaks after disconnecting manifold (test) gauge hoses or any service hoses – see Leak testing.*

Stabilising the system

After connecting a manifold gauge set to the system, and purging the gauge hoses of air (where applicable), the system should be operated for a few minutes to stabilise the pressures and temperatures, and to ensure accurate manifold gauge readings.

To stabilise the system:

1 Start the engine, and run it at a fast idle.

2 Position the air conditioning controls at the maximum cooling position, and set the heater/air conditioning blower to its highest speed **(see illustration)**.

3 Open the vehicle doors and windows to quickly eliminate any heat from the vehicle interior.

4 Operate the system under these conditions for 5 to 10 minutes. The system will then be stabilised, and ready for testing.

With the air conditioning system switched off, the high and low side manifold gauge readings should be approximately equal (approximately 60 psi in the example shown)

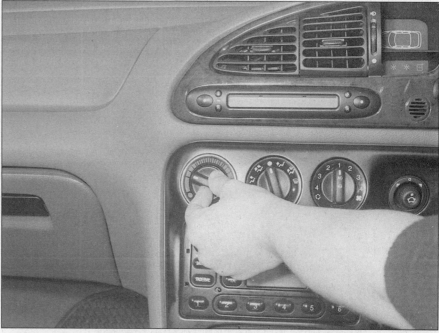

Position the air conditioning controls at the maximum cooling position, and set the heater/air conditioning blower to its highest speed

6

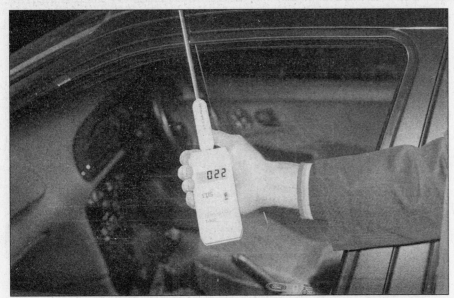

Measure the ambient temperature of the air outside the passenger compartment . . .

Checking the system temperatures and pressures

Once the system has stabilised, it's ready for testing or servicing, but, before carrying out any further work, always check the system temperatures and pressures as follows. Measuring the temperatures and pressures at this stage will give warning of any faults in the system.

1 Using a thermometer, measure the ambient (outside) temperature around the car (ie, measure the temperature of the air outside the passenger compartment). As we've already discussed (Chapter 2), the ambient temperature directly affects the system pressures (particularly the high side pressure). Make a note of the ambient temperature reading (see illustration).

2 Insert a thermometer into the heating/air conditioning system outlet vent inside the vehicle as near as possible to the evaporator (usually one of the centre facia vents). Set the blower motor to its lowest speed, and note the outlet air temperature (see illustration).

3 Note down the high and low side gauge pressure readings.

4 Compare the pressure and temperature readings with those given in the temperature versus pressure charts (shown opposite). Bear in mind that the charts are a guide only, so small deviations from the pressure/ temperature relationships shown can be ignored. If the pressure/temperature relationships differ significantly from those shown, refer to Chapter 7 for details of how to interpret the results.

. . . then measure the air temperature at the outlet vent nearest the evaporator

Pressure/temperature relationship for R12 systems

Low side readings			
Low side pressure gauge reading		Evaporator temperature	
psi	kPa	°F	°C
10	69	2	−17
12	83	6	−14
14	97	10	−12
16	110	14	−10
18	124	18	−8
20	138	20	−7
22	152	22	−6
24	165	24	−4
26	179	27	−3
28	193	29	−2
30	207	32	−0
35	241	36	−2
40	276	42	−6
45	310	48	−9
50	345	53	12
55	379	58	14
60	414	62	17
65	448	66	19
70	483	70	21

High side readings			
High side pressure gauge reading		Ambient temperature	
psi	kPa	°F	°C
130 to 160	896 to 1103	60	16
140 to 170	965 to 1172	65	18
150 to 180	1034 to 1241	70	21
160 to 190	1103 to 1310	75	24
170 to 210	1172 to 1448	80	27
180 to 220	1241 to 1517	85	29
190 to 230	1310 to 1586	90	32
205 to 250	1413 to 1724	95	35
220 to 270	1517 to 1862	100	38
240 to 290	1655 to 2000	105	41
260 to 310	1793 to 2137	110	44
285 to 335	1965 to 2310	115	46
310 to 370	2137 to 2551	120	49

Pressure/temperature relationship for R134a systems

Low side readings			
Low side pressure gauge reading		Evaporator temperature	
psi	kPa	°F	°C
15 to 40	103 to 276	35 to 60	2 to 16
40 to 50	276 to 345	50 to 65	10 to 18

High side readings			
High side pressure gauge reading		Ambient temperature	
psi	kPa	°F	°C
115 to 200	793 to 1379	70 to 80	21 to 27
140 to 235	965 to 1620	80 to 90	27 to 32
165 to 270	1138 to 1861	90 to 100	32 to 38
210 to 310	1448 to 2137	100 to 110	38 to 44

Leak testing

If, after checking the system temperatures and pressures, the refrigerant charge appears to be low, it's worth carrying out a leak test at this stage. Leakage, through loose fittings, deteriorated hoses or seals, or damaged metal lines, is the most common cause of low refrigerant charge. Most leaks are caused by engine vibration, which can loosen threaded fittings, and can cause metal lines to fatigue and crack over a period of time. Tightening connections will often cure leaks, but repair or renewal will be necessary to cure deteriorated hoses or seals, or damaged metal lines. Locating and repairing small leaks can be time consuming, but it's important to ensure that the system is 100% sealed before adding refrigerant.

If possible, leak testing is best carried out when the system contains refrigerant. Leak testing can then be performed with the system switched off, or with the system operating. It's important to realise that some leaks may only occur when the system is operating, and leak testing when evacuating the system, or using pressure testing, will not find these leaks.

When the system contains refrigerant, there are four basic ways of carrying out leak testing (refer to *Pressure testing a system* and *Evacuating a system* for additional methods of leak testing):
a) *Sight.*
b) *Using bubble solution.*
c) *Using tracer dye.*
d) *Using an electronic leak detector.*

When leak testing, always start at the highest points in the system and work down (refrigerants are heavier than air). If testing is started at the bottom of the system, refrigerant may be detected which is actually leaking from a point higher up in the system.
Note: *It is good practice to check the system* *service valves for leaks after disconnecting manifold (test) gauge hoses or any service hoses.*

Leak testing by sight

Look for signs of oil stains around the system components and joints, particularly on the condenser. If oil stains are found, this gives an indication that a leak may be present, and compressor oil has escaped from the system. Note that this check is more relevant to R12 systems which use mineral-based compressor oils. On R134a systems, which use synthetic compressor oils, the oil is less likely to be visible.

Leak testing using bubble solution

This is the cheapest and simplest way to find a leak. Although it can't be relied upon to be 100% effective, this method will often detect leaking connections and joints.
1 Spray or brush a commercial detector solution (or even a soap and water solution)

6

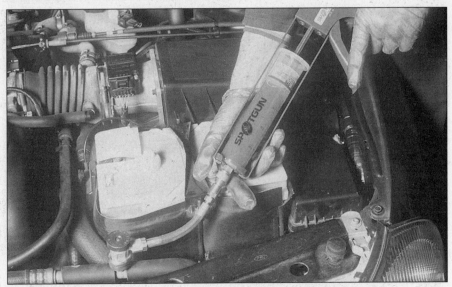

Injecting tracer dye into the system via the low side service valve

onto the suspected leaking area. Most of the commercial detector solutions contain dye to improve visibility.

2 Start the vehicle engine, switch on the air conditioning system, and allow the system to stabilise.

3 Any leaking refrigerant should cause the detector solution to form bubbles around the source of the leak.

4 Tighten the leaking connector, or repair the leaking component (discharge the system before carrying out any repair work), then wipe off the detector solution and repeat the leak testing procedure to ensure that the leak has been fixed.

Leak testing using tracer dye

This method of leak detection involves adding a tracer dye to the refrigerant. This can be done when recharging the system, or at a later date (always follow the manufacturer's recommendations) **(see illustration)**. A few vehicle manufacturers add tracer dye to their systems when the system is first filled with refrigerant at the factory. The brightly-coloured dye is visible under ultra-violet light. Tracer dye can be added to a system when recharging with refrigerant as a matter of course.

To check for leaks, an ultra-violet lamp is shone over the system components **(see illustration)**. Any leaks will then be obvious, showing up as brightly-coloured areas.

 Warning: Always wear suitable eye protection when using an ultra-violet lamp.

Dye injection equipment and purpose-built ultra-violet lamps are available from various manufacturers, and the equipment should always be used in accordance with the manufacturer's instructions.

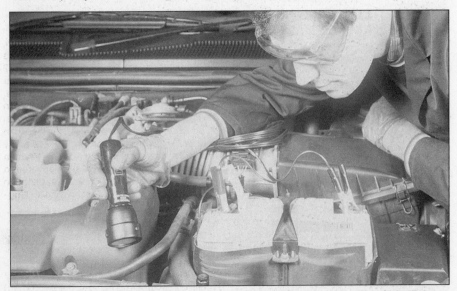

The tracer dye will show up leaks as brightly coloured areas under ultra-violet light

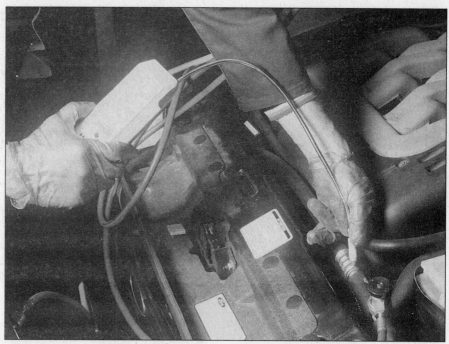

Using an electronic leak detector to search for leaks

Leak testing using an electronic leak detector

Various different types of electronic leak detector are available, but they all tend to work on the same principles. Some units are more sensitive than others, and several different methods of leak indication may be used. The most commonly used method of leak indication is an audible alarm-type warning. Most detectors have a sensing probe which draws air and any leaking refrigerant gas into the detector, and to use the detector, the probe is moved over the system components.

One of the best types of electronic detector is the reset guiding-type. This type of machine allows the sensitivity to be reduced as desired, allowing the user to 'home-in' on the source of a leak. Once a leak has been detected, and the warning reaches a maximum, the sensitivity can be reduced, allowing the machine to be moved closer to the source of the leak before another leak indication is given.

To use an electronic leak detector:

1 Where applicable, make sure that the detector battery is in good condition.

2 Start the vehicle engine, and switch on the air conditioning system.

3 Search for leaks (starting at the highest points of the system) by slowly moving the sensing probe over all the system components **(see illustration)**.

4 If a leak is detected, where possible try to home-in to find the exact source. If it proves difficult to locate the precise source of the leak, once the general area has been located, it may be possible to use a bubble solution or tracer dye to find the exact source, as described previously.

Identifying the refrigerant in the system

⚠️ *Warning: Some vehicles (eg, some Ford, Peugeot and Volvo models) may have a system which is fitted with R12 service valves, but is actually charged with R134a. Some vehicles may also be encountered which have R12 systems which have been retrofitted to use R134a. Normally, these systems will have a prominent label or plate fitted under the bonnet, or on the compressor, to indicate that they are filled with R134a.*

Before attempting to discharge a system, or add refrigerant to a system, it's sensible to identify the refrigerant already in the system. Never assume that because a system has R12 connections it has been filled with R12 refrigerant, and similarly, never assume that an R134a system has been filled with R134a. It's always possible that the system has been filled with the wrong refrigerant, or that an alternative aftermarket refrigerant other than R12 or R134a has been used. If there's any doubt as to the type or purity of refrigerant in the system, it should always be recovered to a waste cylinder – don't risk contamination by recovering to a cylinder of good refrigerant.

There are two ways of identifying refrigerants; by using a refrigerant comparator, or by using an electronic refrigerant gas analyser. A good gas analyser will provide more conclusive results, but the equipment can be expensive.

6

Using a refrigerant comparator (slide rule)

Note: *A refrigerant comparator can only be used accurately to identify refrigerant when the refrigerant is in a saturated state, ie, liquid and vapour are present. If a comparator is not available, the refrigerant temperature/pressure charts in Chapter 8 will provide a guide to refrigerant temperature/pressure relationships.*

To identify the refrigerant in a system using a refrigerant comparator, the following tools are required.

a) *A set of manifold (test) gauges.*
b) *An accurate thermometer.*
c) *A comparator (slide rule type).*

1 Ensure that the air conditioning system is switched off, and that the vehicle engine is stopped.

2 Connect a set of manifold gauges to the system as described previously (ensure that the gauge low side hose has been purged of air).

3 Note the pressure indicated on the low side gauge (the pressures indicated on both gauges should be the same, but reading from the low side gauge will give greater accuracy due to the larger divisions on the scale).

4 Using an accurate thermometer with a suitable probe, measure the temperature at the bottom of the condenser. If possible, push the probe into the condenser fins, but take care not to damage them. Provided the air conditioning system is switched off the temperature of the fins should be at almost the same temperature as the liquid refrigerant in the bottom of the condenser.

5 Using the comparator, slide the cursor along the pressure line until the fixed line on the cursor is aligned with the pressure measured on the low side gauge **(see illustration)**. By referring to the temperature scales on the comparator (there is usually a temperature scale for each refrigerant type), it should be possible to identify the refrigerant; check to see on which refrigerant temperature scale the fixed cursor line is aligned with the appropriate temperature (the refrigerant temperature/ pressure data charts in Chapter 8 will provide a guide if a comparator is not available). Be wary, because at certain pressures, R12 refrigerant will be at the same temperature as R134a refrigerant; in this case, the two refrigerants can be distinguished using a halide torch in accordance with the manufacturer's instructions, but this is not to be recommended as it produces a toxic gas, and involves deliberately venting refrigerant (although, a very small amount) to the atmosphere, which is an offence.

⚠️ *Warning: Using a halide torch can be dangerous; R12 and R134a refrigerant both produce lethally poisonous gases when in the presence of a naked flame. Always use a halide torch exactly in accordance with the manufacturer's instructions, in a well-ventilated area. Do not use a halide torch for leak detection work.*

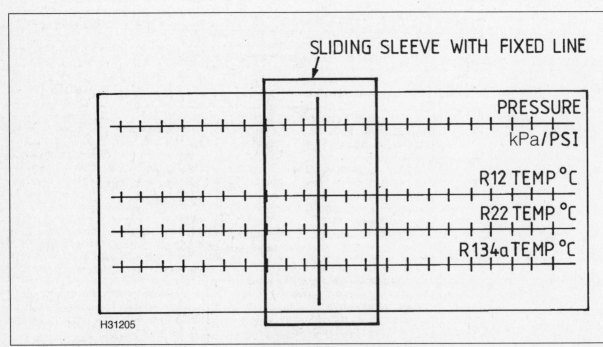

H31205

Refrigerant comparator (slide rule)

Using an electronic refrigerant gas analyser

These machines should always be used exactly in accordance with the manufacturer's instructions to avoid damage to the equipment and inaccurate results.

Most analysers work by drawing in a vapour sample (liquid refrigerant and compressor oil will damage most analysers – refer to the manufacturer's recommendations for details), analysing the sample, and then producing a read-out of the analysis. To obtain pure refrigerant vapour, it may be necessary to draw refrigerant from the system into a clean cylinder, and sample from the cylinder.

Analysers usually provide a read-out of the percentage purity of the refrigerant, and details of any contamination or mixing of refrigerants, and any air or moisture present (see illustration).

Compressor oils

As we've already seen in Chapter 2, compressor oil is an essential part of the system, and without sufficient oil, a compressor will fail very quickly. We've also seen that the oil and the refrigerant mix together, and are pumped around the system by the compressor. This means that although a high proportion of the oil will be in the compressor at any one time, a proportion of the oil will be circulating around the other system components. This in turn means that if there is a refrigerant leak, or if the

system is discharged, some oil will also be lost from the system.

So it's important to check the compressor oil level whenever any work is carried out which involves discharging the refrigerant and opening the system, or when there has been a refrigerant leak. Bear in mind that if two or three refrigerant recharges are carried out without adding any compressor oil, the system will have been discharged two or three times, which could mean that all the compressor oil has been lost.

Remember that R12 systems use mineral oil, and R134a systems use PAG oil. Using the wrong oil will wreck the compressor very quickly. Both oils are available in a range of grades (viscosities), although most R12 system compressors use the same grade of oil. Always check the manufacturer's recommendations, and the Specifications provided in Chapter 8, to ensure that the correct type and viscosity of oil is used.

For a vehicle air conditioning system which requires 200 cc of compressor oil (this is a typical figure, always check the vehicle manufacturer's recommendations to find the actual figure), when the system is new, the compressor will contain 200 cc of oil. However, once the air conditioning system has been run, the oil will be distributed around the system with the refrigerant. Typically, the oil distribution may be as follows:

Typical electronic refrigerant gas analyser

6

Rule of thumb guide for compressor oil distribution around a system

Compressor	*116 cc*
Condenser	*28 cc*
Filter/drier or accumulator	*14 cc*
Evaporator	*28 cc*
Pipes and hoses	*14 cc*

Note also that some oil (possibly 50 cc, or so) is likely to be absorbed by the desiccant in the filter/drier or accumulator. From this we can see that if, say the system is discharged, and a new condenser is fitted, 28 cc of oil is likely to be lost when the old condenser is scrapped, and some oil will be lost with the refrigerant when the system is discharged. It will therefore be essential to add some compressor oil when the system is recharged.

It's important to note that since the oil distributes itself throughout the system during operation, it isn't absolutely necessary to add the oil to the component being replaced. With the exception of the compressor, if a component is being removed, provided the amount of oil lost during the removal procedure is added to the system somewhere, the compressor will be fine. If, however, the compressor is removed, always add the new oil to the compressor, and nowhere else, otherwise the compressor may be dry when it starts which will cause serious damage very quickly.

Obviously, before oil is added to a system, it's important to have an idea of how much oil is already present in the system.

Note: *Compressor oils, particularly PAG oils are very hygroscopic – ie, they absorb water. To prevent problems, compressor oil containers must always be tightly sealed, and should not be left open to atmosphere. Some compressor oil manufacturers recommend that* the oil is discarded if it is left open to the atmosphere for more than 20 minutes! Similarly, whenever system components are disconnected, the open pipes and components should be sealed immediately (cover or plug the openings) to minimise the entry of moisture.

Checking and topping up the compressor oil level

Note: *Maintaining the correct compressor oil level is essential to prevent failure of the compressor. Measuring the quantity of compressor oil present in an air conditioning system is an imprecise science, and no single procedure applies to all systems. Many vehicles are fitted with an air conditioning system specifications plate or label, usually under the bonnet, which provides details of the system refrigerant type and quantity, and the recommended compressor oil type and (sometimes) quantity. If no specifications plate or label is fitted, it's important to follow the compressor manufacturer's or vehicle manufacturer's recommendations for oil type and quantity. The following information is intended only as a guide. Refer to Chapter 8 for details of compressor oil capacities.*

There are many different designs of compressor in use, so unfortunately there's no single method of checking the amount of oil in a system which applies to all compressors.

Most refrigerant handling machines have a facility for separating compressor oil from the refrigerant when the system is discharged. The oil is collected in a reservoir, and the oil level can be read off from a scale. Note however, that some oil will remain in the system when the system has been discharged, so the oil recovered will not be the total quantity of oil in the system. Many machines also provide a facility for adding oil when charging the system with refrigerant. Always follow the equipment manufacturer's instructions.

If the oil drained from the system contains metal chips or other foreign material, remove the accumulator or receiver/drier (as applicable), flush the system and fit a new accumulator or receiver/drier and expansion valve or orifice tube. Also renew any other components which may have been damaged.

The following information will provide a guide, when working on a typical system, but always follow the vehicle manufacturer's recommendations for specific details.

Checking compressor oil level using a dipstick

This method of oil checking can only be used on compressor designs featuring an oil sump, and an oil level checking aperture (which will be sealed by a removable bolt).

⚠ **Warning: Before checking compressor oil level using a dipstick, the system MUST be discharged. If the system is not discharged, the refrigerant pressure will blow out the sump plug, which could not only cause injury, but will also discharge the system into the atmosphere.**

Once the system has been discharged, locate the oil level checking aperture bolt, and proceed as follows.

1 Unscrew the checking aperture bolt from the compressor.

2 On some piston-type compressors, it may be necessary to turn the rotor to position the connecting rods and/or squish-plate so that the dipstick can pass down into the sump **(see illustration)**.

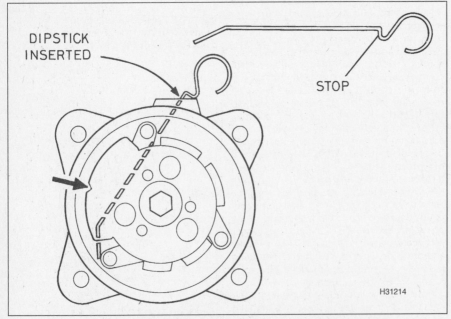

DIPSTICK INSERTED

STOP

H31214

Using a dipstick to check the oil level on a Sanden 5-cylinder compressor

Note the position of the notch (arrowed) on the compressor front plate

3 Consult the compressor manufacturer's information for details of the type of dipstick required, and how to use it.

4 Slide the dipstick down into the compressor sump, then withdraw it and read off the oil level **(see illustration)**. Wipe off the dipstick, and re-check the oil level to confirm the reading.

5 If necessary, add oil to the compressor. Bear in mind that, as mentioned previously, some oil will be present in the other system components (condenser, evaporator and pipework), so don't add the full amount of oil required to bring the compressor oil level up to its recommended level, or you may effectively overfill the compressor. It isn't possible to measure the exact amount of oil present in the system, so an estimate will have to be made as to the amount of oil distributed around the system components.

6 Once the appropriate amount of oil has been added to the compressor, refit the sump plug.

7 Charge the system with refrigerant (see *Charging a system with refrigerant*).

Checking compressor oil level by removing compressor and tipping out oil

This method of oil level checking is not always possible, or desirable, as it involves removing the compressor. Note that this method can only be used on compressors incorporating an oil sump. Many compressors have no oil sump, and are designed to retain very little oil when the system is not operating.

1 After discharging the system, remove the compressor.

2 Drain the oil from the compressor into a graduated measuring cylinder.

3 When the oil has finished draining, read off the oil quantity from the measuring cylinder.

4 Compare the quantity of oil drained with the recommended oil capacity of the compressor. Bear in mind that, as mentioned previously, some oil will be present in the other system components (condenser, evaporator and pipework), so don't add the full amount of oil required to bring the compressor oil level up to its recommended level, or you may effectively overfill the compressor. It isn't possible to measure the exact amount of oil present in the system, so an estimate will have to be made as to the amount of oil distributed around the system components (see *Rule of thumb guide for compressor oil distribution around a system*). Although it may not be desirable due to the work involved, it's possible to remove the evaporator, condenser and accumulator or filter/drier (as applicable) and drain the oil from them into a measuring cylinder in order to determine the total quantity of oil in the system.

5 Pour the required quantity of oil into the compressor **(see illustration)**. Although it's possible to re-use the oil drained into the measuring cylinder, it's advisable to use new oil (particularly on R134a systems – the PAG

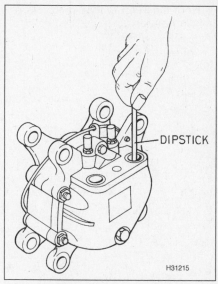

Using a dipstick to check the oil level on a York rotary van compressor

oil rapidly absorbs moisture from the atmosphere).

6 Refit the compressor, then charge the system with refrigerant (see *Charging a system with refrigerant*).

Compressors with no oil sump

 Warning: Since this type of compressor has no sump, it must be well lubricated. If the compressor runs dry, it will be destroyed.

Compressors which have no oil sump retain very little oil, and therefore the amount of oil in the system cannot be measured directly by considering the amount of oil in the compressor. However, there are a few guidelines which can be followed when working with this type of compressor.

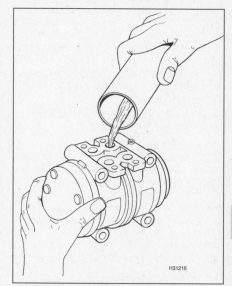

Refilling a Nippondenso 10-cylinder compressor with oil

6

1 When renewing components (even if no leak is suspected).

a) *If a new compressor is being fitted, remove the old compressor, drain and measure the oil, and add the measured amount of fresh oil to the new compressor. Add an extra 28 cc or so of oil to the new compressor to compensate for any oil lost during the removal procedure.*

b) *If the evaporator, condenser, or accumulator or filter/drier (as applicable) are renewed, drain any oil from the old component(s) and add the measured quantity of fresh oil to the new component(s).*

2 When there is a minor loss of refrigerant over a period of time.

a) *If a component is being renewed to cure the leak, add compressor oil to the component in accordance with the* Rule of thumb guide for compressor oil distribution around a system *given in the introduction to this Section.*

b) *If the source of the leak is traced to a fault which does not require renewal of one of the major system components (such as a leaking seal in a refrigerant line), add a small amount of refrigerant oil (28 cc, for example) to the system when it is recharged.*

3 When there's evidence of a major leak, or if the oil level is unknown, and the system performance and efficiency is marginal.

Drain and flush the system, and add the full recommended quantity of compressor oil to the compressor or system components, as applicable.

Fitting a new compressor

New compressors may be supplied pre-filled with fresh oil; if so, don't assume that it's the correct amount. If a new compressor is being fitted (in which case a new accumulator or filter/drier should be fitted), drain and measure the quantity of oil inside before fitting it. Do not add more than the specified amount of oil to the compressor before fitting, and bear in mind that unless the system has been flushed, some oil will remain in the other system components.

Adding oil to a system when charging with refrigerant

If desired, oil can be added to a system when charging with refrigerant. It's advisable to do this, even if none of the system components have been disturbed, because as we've already discussed, some oil will have been lost when the system was discharged. As mentioned previously, many refrigerant handling machines have a facility for adding compressor oil; the following details will provide a guide when using basic equipment for recharging.

To add oil as the system is charged, a suitable oil cylinder and fittings will be required to connect to the system. The oil can either be added after evacuating the system, before recharging with refrigerant, or during the recharging process. A suitable oil charging cylinder will be required.

1 Pour the required quantity of oil into a charging cylinder, then connect the charging cylinder to the system in accordance with the manufacturer's instructions. Depending on the equipment used, the charging cylinder should be connected either directly to the low side service port (with the system holding vacuum), or between the service (yellow) hose, which should be connected to a refrigerant cylinder for charging, and the manifold gauge set **(see illustration)**.

2 Charge the system with oil according to the equipment manufacturer's instructions. If the oil is being added during refrigerant charging, refer to *Charging a system with refrigerant*, noting that additional hand valves will probably have to be opened on the oil cylinder to allow oil and refrigerant into the system. As the system is charged with refrigerant, the oil will be drawn into the system.

Discharging a system

When is discharging necessary?

Whenever the system has to be 'opened' to allow repairs or removal of any part, the refrigerant must first be safely discharged from the system. In addition to being a safety precaution, discharging is a legal requirement, as it's an offence to intentionally vent refrigerant into the atmosphere.

A system must also be discharged if it's suspected that there is any contamination in the refrigerant circuit.

Adding compressor oil via a charging cylinder connected directly to the low side service port

Reclaiming and recycling refrigerant

When a system is discharged, the refrigerant must be either reclaimed, or recycled, via a refrigerant recovery machine (a recovery machine simply pumps refrigerant from a system into a container).

Reclaiming is not the same as recycling. Refrigerant recycling can be carried out using a recycling machine in the workshop, but reclaiming can only be carried out by an approved refrigerant waste handler using highly specialised equipment.

Before discharging a system, the refrigerant should be identified as described previously. If an electronic analyser has been used, it may indicate whether the refrigerant is suitable for recycling, or whether the refrigerant should be considered as waste for reclaiming.

Many refrigerant handling machines incorporate both recovery and recycling equipment.

⚠ *Warning: Unless otherwise stated by the manufacturers, separate recovery/recycling equipment must be used for R12 and R134a refrigerant, and separate storage cylinders must always be used. R12 refrigerant must not under any circumstances be recovered/recycled using R134a equipment and vice versa. If recovery/recycling equipment is contaminated with the wrong refrigerant, the equipment could effectively be rendered useless.*

Reclaiming refrigerant

To reclaim refrigerant, a recovery machine will be required to pump the refrigerant from the system into a waste refrigerant (reclaim) cylinder. A single waste cylinder can be used for all waste gases, regardless of type.

⚠ *Warning: Do not exceed the recommended maximum fill capacity for a refrigerant cylinder. Refer to Filling a container with refrigerant for details of how to ensure that a cylinder is not overfilled.*

Once a refrigerant reclaim cylinder has been filled to its maximum capacity, it should be returned to a registered waste refrigerant handler for reclaiming or disposal.

Recycling refrigerant

To recycle refrigerant, a recycling machine will be required. Most recycling machines incorporate a recovery machine to pump the refrigerant from the system for recycling, and a recycling cylinder to store the recycled refrigerant. If it's necessary to use separate refrigerant recycling cylinders, ensure that separate cylinders are used for R12 and R134a refrigerant. Never allow R12 refrigerant to contaminate an R134a recycling cylinder, and *vice versa.*

A recycling machine cleans and dries refrigerant so that it can be re-used. The refrigerant is pumped through separation chambers and filters which remove oil and particles of contamination. The refrigerant then passes through a drier to remove moisture, and passes to a storage cylinder where it is stored for re-use. Single-pass and multi-pass recycling machines are available; in a multi-pass machine, the refrigerant is run through the filtering and drying process several times.

Discharging a system safely

Once the refrigerant in the system has been identified, the system can be discharged, and the refrigerant collected in a recycling cylinder or reclaim (waste) cylinder, as appropriate.

Always follow the equipment manufacturer's instructions when using refrigerant recovery and/or recycling equipment. The following procedure will act as a guide when using basic recovery equipment connected to the system via a manifold gauge set.

Note: *Most recovery/recycling machines are fitted with a moisture indicator, which will indicate when the moisture filter on the machine is saturated. If the filter is saturated, the machine will be unable to remove any moisture from the refrigerant. Always change the filter if the moisture indicator shows that it is saturated.*

1 With the vehicle engine stopped, and a manifold gauge set connected to the system as described previously (see *Preliminary work*), proceed as follows.

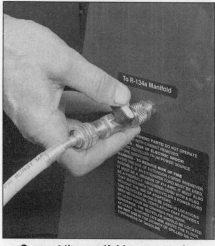

Connect the manifold gauge service hose . . .

2 Connect the manifold gauge service (yellow) hose to the inlet port of the recovery machine **(see illustrations)**.

3 Connect the recovery machine outlet hose to a suitable refrigerant cylinder (a recycling cylinder or reclaim cylinder, as appropriate). Note that if a dual-port cylinder is used, the hose can be connected to either port.

⚠ *Warning: Do not exceed the recommended maximum fill capacity for a refrigerant cylinder. Refer to Filling a container with refrigerant for details of how to ensure that a cylinder is not overfilled.*

. . . to the inlet port of the recovery/refrigerant handling machine

6

4 Where necessary, carefully purge the air from the manifold gauge hoses and the recovery machine-to-refrigerant cylinder hose, in accordance with the equipment manufacturer's instructions.

5 Open the high and low side manifold gauge hand valves, any appropriate valves on the recovery machine, and the valve on the refrigerant cylinder.

6 Check to make sure that all valves between the system and the refrigerant cylinder are open, then switch on the recovery machine.

7 Run the recovery machine until a zero reading is indicated on both manifold gauges, then continue to run the machine until a slight vacuum is indicated on the low side gauge **(see illustration)**. This will ensure that all the refrigerant is removed from the system.

8 Stop the recovery machine, then close all the valves between the system and the refrigerant cylinder.

Note: *On completion of recovery, the pressure indicated on the manifold gauges may rise, and there may be a hissing sound from the system. This is normal, and is due to a small amount of dissolved refrigerant vapour being released from the compressor oil remaining in the system. Similarly, a hissing sound may be heard when disconnecting system connections once the system has been discharged.*

Pressure testing a system

Once an air conditioning system has been discharged, pressure testing can be carried out at any time as a method of leak testing. Even if there is no obvious sign of leakage, the system should always be pressure tested prior to evacuation and recharging to ensure that the system is gas-tight.

Note: *Pressure testing a system will not provide conclusive proof that a system is leak-free. Even though the system holds pressure when it is not operating, the system may leak when operating (it is not possible to pressure test to the operating pressure on the high side of the system), or under a vacuum. Refer to* Preliminary work *at the beginning of this Chapter, and to* Evacuating a system *for details of alternative methods of leak-detection.*

Oxygen-Free Nitrogen (OFN)

The **only** medium suitable for pressure-testing an air conditioning system is oxygen-free nitrogen (OFN). NEVER attempt to pressure test a system using refrigerant, air, water, or anything else other than OFN. The reason for using OFN is that it is harmless to the air conditioning system and the environment; it does not contain any moisture, and can be vented into the atmosphere without any harmful effects to health or the environment.

OFN is normally stored under high pressure in cylinders. When using OFN for pressure testing an air conditioning system, it's important to fit the OFN cylinder with a suitable pressure regulator to avoid excessive pressures which could damage the system components. A pressure regulator with a maximum setting of 150 psi (1034 kPa) is ideal. Always use OFN equipment in accordance with the manufacturer's instructions.

 Warning: NEVER attempt to run an air conditioning system using OFN instead of refrigerant, as irreparable damage will be caused to the compressor.

Using OFN to pressure-test a system

1 With a manifold gauge set connected to the system as described previously (see *Preliminary work*), proceed as follows.

2 Connect the manifold gauge service (yellow) hose to the OFN supply.

3 Open the high and low side manifold gauge hand valves.

4 Open the main valve on the OFN cylinder, then turn the regulator to give a maximum pressure of around 50 psi (345 kPa) on the regulator gauge. Note that the operating pressure on the high side of the system may be up to 300 psi (2069 kPa), so pressure testing will not provide conclusive proof that the system is leak-free under operating pressures.

Warning: Do not pressure test the system using high pressure OFN, as damage may be caused to the components on the low side of the air conditioning system (particularly the evaporator, which is designed to operate at relatively low pressures).

5 Work around the system, and listen for a leak. If you can hear a leak, if necessary use one of the methods described previously (see *Preliminary work*) to locate the exact source.

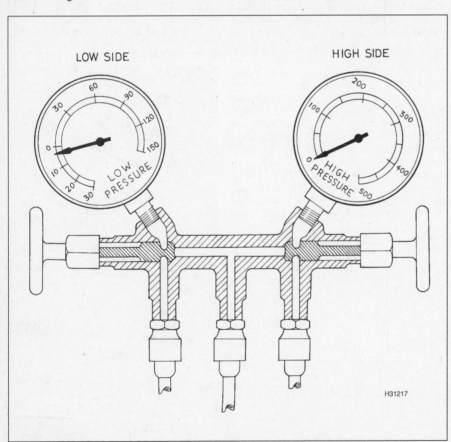

Run the recovery machine until a zero reading is indicated on the high side gauge, and a slight vacuum is indicated on the low side gauge

6 If there is no audible sign of leakage, shut the main valve on the OFN cylinder, then leave the system for a few minutes to see if the pressure on the gauges is maintained.

7 If pressure is maintained, the system is likely to be leak-free, and is ready for recharging. If the system loses pressure, there's a leak which should be located (see *Preliminary work*) and fixed.

Evacuating a system

Once a system has been discharged, and any work on the system components has been completed, the system must be completely evacuated using a vacuum pump (see Chapter 4 for further details) to remove all traces of moisture before recharging with refrigerant.

Any moisture is very harmful to air conditioning systems. Moisture can freeze in the system, restricting the flow of refrigerant, and moisture also reacts with the refrigerant to produce acids, which damage the system internal components. Moisture in the system can also lead to excessive system pressures.

Every system is equipped with a filter/drier or an accumulator to trap and retain moisture which invariably finds its way into the system in service, but it's vital to removal all air from the system before recharging. We saw in Chapter 1 that air contains moisture, so even the slightest leak will allow air and moisture into the system.

Evacuating a system will also act as a leak check; if the system does not hold vacuum, there must be a leak.

Using a vacuum pump to evacuate a system

Before using a vacuum pump, ensure that the system has been discharged (see *Discharging a system*).

Always follow the manufacturer's instructions when using a vacuum pump. Most refrigerant handling machines will have a built-in vacuum pump. The following procedure will act as a guide when using a vacuum pump connected to the system via a manifold gauge set.

1 Ensure that the system has been discharged, and all work on the system components has been completed. With a manifold gauge set connected to the system as described previously (see *Preliminary work*), proceed as follows.

2 Connect the manifold gauge service (yellow) hose to the inlet port of the vacuum pump (see illustration).

3 Open the manifold gauge high and low side hand valves as far as possible.

4 Note the reading on the low side manifold gauge, then switch on the vacuum pump. If, after a couple of minutes, no vacuum is indicated on the low side gauge, check gauge hose connections, and check the system for leaks. Cure any problems before proceeding.

5 After approximately 10 minutes, close the high and low side manifold gauge hand valves, then stop the vacuum pump. Note the reading on the low side manifold gauge, which should be approaching 760 mm Hg (30 in Hg) – a perfect vacuum at sea level, so the reading will never actually reach this figure) **(see illustration)**.

6 Leave the system for about 5 minutes, and check the reading on the low side manifold gauge. The gauge reading should not change, indicating that the system is holding vacuum (note that this is not conclusive proof that the system is not leaking). If the gauge reading moves back towards zero, this indicates a leak somewhere in the system which is causing a loss of vacuum.

Connect the manifold gauge service hose to the inlet port of a vacuum pump

7 If the system is losing vacuum, disconnect the vacuum pump from the system, and check for leaks, as described previously (see *Preliminary work* and *Pressure testing a system*). Once the leak has been found and fixed, repeat the evacuation procedure.

8 If the system holds vacuum, open the high and low side manifold gauge hand valves again, and restart the vacuum pump. After approximately 30 minutes (no less – this should ensure that all moisture is removed from the system, although if the system has been left open to atmosphere for a long time, an extended vacuuming period is advisable), close the high and low side gauge hand valves, then stop the vacuum pump. The system is now ready for recharging.

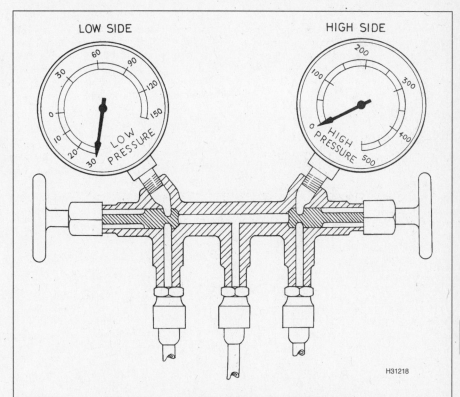

After approximately 10 minutes of evacuation, the reading on the low side manifold gauge should be approaching 760 mm Hg (30 in Hg)

6

Filling a container with refrigerant

When refrigerant is being transferred into a storage cylinder, safety must always be the first consideration. If a refrigerant cylinder is overfilled, the cylinder can burst with catastrophic results.

The capacity of a refrigerant cylinder is measured by weight. All safety-approved refrigerant storage cylinders are marked with a 'Tare' weight (the weight of the empty cylinder, complete with its valve or valves), and maximum refrigerant fill weights for both virgin and waste (or recycled) refrigerant. If you come across a container which is not marked with a Tare weight and/or maximum refrigerant fill weights, **DO NOT** use it; the cylinder is likely to be sub-standard, and may not be safe.

The maximum fill weight for waste (or recycled) refrigerant will always be lower than the maximum fill weight for virgin refrigerant, because with waste (or recycled) refrigerant more space must be allowed in the cylinder for refrigerant vapours to be released from the compressor oil which will be present in the waste (or recycled) refrigerant.

Transferring virgin refrigerant from a large to a smaller cylinder

Note: A set of accurate scales will be required for this procedure. Do not use a recovery machine to transfer virgin refrigerant from one cylinder to another, as the refrigerant may absorb oil from the machine, leading to contamination.

The easiest way of transferring refrigerant from a large cylinder to a smaller one is to cool the smaller cylinder, in a fridge for example. The larger cylinder can be heated, but cooling the smaller cylinder is more efficient, and normally far easier.

1 Cool the smaller refrigerant cylinder to give a reasonable temperature differential between the large and the smaller cylinder, then proceed as follows.

2 Look on the smaller refrigerant cylinder, and note the Tare weight of the cylinder, and the maximum fill weight for the particular refrigerant in question (R12 or R134a). Add the Tare weight to the refrigerant maximum fill weight, to give the maximum permissible overall weight for the cylinder.

eg:

Tare weight (TWT) of cylinder =
    8.2 kg

Maximum fill weight of virgin R134a =
    13.9 kg

Maximum permissible overall weight =
    22.1 kg

3 Connect a suitable refrigerant hose between the valves on the large and smaller cylinder. If the larger cylinder is a dual-port type, connect the hose to the liquid (red) port.

4 Zero the scales, then place the smaller cylinder on the scales. Compare the weight indicated on the scales with the Tare weight of the cylinder. Bear in mind that the weight of the refrigerant hose will affect the weight indicated. If the weight indicated is significantly higher than the Tare weight, it will be because the smaller cylinder already contains some refrigerant.

5 Open the valves to allow refrigerant to flow from the large cylinder to the smaller cylinder, but make sure that the weight indicated on the scales does not exceed the maximum permissible overall weight for the cylinder (22.1 kg in the above example) **(see illustration)**. Note that if desired, by watching the reading on the scales, a measured quantity (weight) of refrigerant can be transferred to the smaller cylinder.

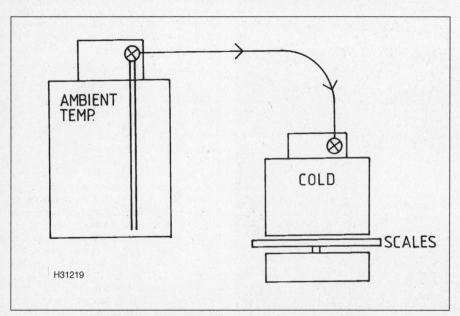

Transferring refrigerant from a large to a smaller cylinder

Filling a cylinder with waste or recycled refrigerant

To fill a reclaim (waste) or recycling cylinder with refrigerant, proceed as follows.

1 Look on the refrigerant cylinder, and note the Tare weight of the cylinder, and the maximum fill weight for waste refrigerant of the particular type in question (R12 or R134a). Add the Tare weight to the waste refrigerant maximum fill weight, to give the maximum permissible overall weight of the cylinder.

eg:

Tare weight (TWT) of cylinder =
    8.2 kg

Maximum fill weight of virgin R134a =
    13.9 kg

Maximum fill weight of waste R134a =
    Maximum fill weight of virgin R134a
    x 75%

Maximum overall weight =
    8.2 kg + (13.9 kg x 75%) =
    8.2 kg + 10.4 kg =
    18.6 kg

2 Zero the scales, then place the refrigerant cylinder on the scales. Compare the weight indicated on the scales with the Tare weight of the container. Bear in mind that the weight of the refrigerant hose will affect the weight indicated. If the weight indicated is significantly higher than the Tare weight, it will be because the cylinder already contains some refrigerant.

3 Discharge the system into the refrigerant cylinder using a recovery machine, as described previously (see *Discharging a system*), but make sure that the weight indicated on the scales does not exceed the maximum permissible overall weight for the cylinder (18.6 kg in the above example).

Charging a system with refrigerant

Before recharging a system, there are three important operations which must be carried out first:

Typical air conditioning system specifications label

1) *Where possible, the compressor oil level must be checked (see* Compressor oils*).*
2) *The system should have been leak tested to ensure that there are no leaks (see* Preliminary work *and* Pressure testing a system*).*
3) *The system must be evacuated to remove any moisture (see* Evacuating a system*).*

When charging a system, the vehicle manufacturer's recommendations should always be followed if possible. Charging is carried out via the system service valve(s).

There are two basic alternative methods of charging a system; vapour charging, or liquid charging. Vapour charging is generally carried out on the low side of a system, whereas liquid charging is generally carried out on the high side of a system. If the layout of the system being charged allows a choice between vapour or liquid charging, vapour charging is always preferable because it is safer than liquid charging.

Always make sure that the system is charged with the correct type of refrigerant (either R12 or R134a).

Vapour charging

If a refrigerant handling machine is being used, always work in accordance with the equipment manufacturer's instructions. The following procedure will act as a guide when using basic equipment, charging the system directly from a refrigerant cylinder, via a manifold gauge set.

Once the system has been leak tested and evacuated (the system should be holding a vacuum at the start of the charging process), proceed as follows. Leave the manifold gauge set connected to the system to carry out charging.

⚠ *Warning: Ensure that sufficient compressor oil is present in the system before proceeding. This procedure uses the compressor to draw refrigerant into the system – if there is insufficient compressor oil in the system, the compressor could be seriously damaged.*

1 Gently warm the refrigerant cylinder using a purpose-made electric heating belt, or a container of warm water. Do not heat the cylinder excessively, and **NEVER** use a naked flame. Warming the cylinder will increase the pressure of the refrigerant inside, which will allow it to flow into the system more easily.

2 Check the air conditioning system Specifications label on the vehicle to find the recommended refrigerant quantity for the vehicle being worked on **(see illustration)**. Remember to make allowance for the fact that the hose between the manifold gauge set and the service valve on the vehicle will have to fill with refrigerant before any can enter the system (the service hose between the refrigerant cylinder and the manifold gauge set will fill when air is bled from the hose at the start of the procedure). As a very rough guide it's probably wise to allow for approximately 30 g of refrigerant per metre of hose (ie, in

6

addition to the recommended charge weight, for every metre of hose, add an extra 30 g of refrigerant). Note that this amount of refrigerant is often allowed for in the manufacturer's refrigerant charge specification tolerance. If the specified charge weight is unknown, always err on the low side – a system will operate with a low charge, but there is a risk of injury and damage to the system components if the system is overcharged.

3 Place the refrigerant cylinder on the scales, and check that there is sufficient refrigerant in the cylinder to carry out a complete charge. Weigh the cylinder, then subtract the Tare weight of the cylinder to determine how much refrigerant is in the cylinder.

eg:

Total weight of cylinder =	13.7 kg
Tare weight of cylinder =	8.2 kg
Weight of refrigerant in cylinder =	5.5 kg

4 Assuming that there is sufficient refrigerant in the cylinder, leave the cylinder standing on the scales, then connect the manifold gauge service (yellow) hose to the cylinder. If a dual-port refrigerant cylinder is being used, use the blue (low pressure vapour) valve for vapour charging. If the cylinder has only one valve, stand the cylinder upright for vapour charging.

5 Once the manifold gauge service hose has been connected, open the valve on the refrigerant cylinder and, where necessary, carefully purge the air from the manifold gauge service hose, in accordance with the manufacturer's recommendations.

6 Zero the scales.

7 Open the low side (blue) manifold gauge hand valve. Leave the high side (red) hand valve shut.

8 Start the vehicle engine, and switch on the air conditioning system. This will start the compressor, and draw the refrigerant vapour into the system.

9 Watch the reading on the scales, and when the correct weight of refrigerant has been sucked into the system, close the valve on the refrigerant cylinder. Wait for a few seconds, then close the low side manifold gauge valve.

Note: *On orifice tube-type systems it may take a long time to charge the system because the low-pressure cut-out switch (see Chapter 2) will cause the compressor to cycle on and off as the system pressure drops. To prevent this from happening, and to speed up the charging process, the low pressure switch wiring connector can be disconnected, and the connector terminals can be bridged with a jumper wire. If this is done, ensure that the jumper wire is removed, and the switch wiring connector is reconnected, as soon as the system has been charged.*

10 When charging is complete, stop the vehicle engine, and disconnect the manifold gauge service hose from the refrigerant cylinder. Take care, as a small amount of refrigerant will be released as the hose is disconnected.

11 On completion, before disconnecting the manifold gauge set, check the system temperatures and pressures, and check the performance of the system, as described previously in *Preliminary work*.

12 Once the manifold gauge set has been disconnected, it's advisable to check for leaks around the system service valves – see *Leak testing*.

Liquid charging

If a refrigerant handling machine is being used, always work in accordance with the equipment manufacturer's instructions. The following procedure will act as a guide when using basic equipment, charging the system directly from a refrigerant liquid charging cylinder, via a manifold gauge set.

Once the system has been pressure tested and evacuated (the system should be holding a vacuum at the start of the charging process), proceed as follows. Leave the manifold gauge set connected to the system to carry out charging.

1 Evacuate the liquid charging cylinder using a vacuum pump.

2 Gently warm the refrigerant source cylinder using a purpose-made electric heating belt, or a container of warm water. Do not heat the cylinder excessively, and **NEVER** use a naked flame. Warming the cylinder will increase the pressure of the refrigerant inside, which will allow it to flow into the liquid charging cylinder more easily.

3 Connect a suitable hose between the refrigerant source cylinder and the charging cylinder. If a dual-port refrigerant source cylinder is being used, connect the hose to the red (high pressure liquid) valve. If a single-port refrigerant source cylinder is being used, connect the hose to the port, then invert the cylinder to ensure that liquid refrigerant is delivered to the charging cylinder **(see illustration)**.

4 Open the valve on the refrigerant source cylinder, and carefully purge air from the source cylinder-to-charging cylinder hose, according to the manufacturer's instructions. DO NOT open the charging cylinder valve to do this, as vacuum will be lost, and air will be sucked into the charging cylinder.

5 Check the air conditioning system Specifications label on the vehicle, or the *Specifications* in Chapter 8, to find the recommended refrigerant quantity for the vehicle being worked on.

6 Check the capacity of the charging cylinder to determine approximately how much refrigerant should be allowed to enter the cylinder to enable the system to be charged fully. Ensure that a little more refrigerant than necessary is allowed to enter the cylinder.

7 Open the source cylinder valve, and the charging cylinder inlet valve, and allow the desired quantity of refrigerant to enter the charging cylinder.

8 Close the source cylinder valve when the desired amount of refrigerant has entered the

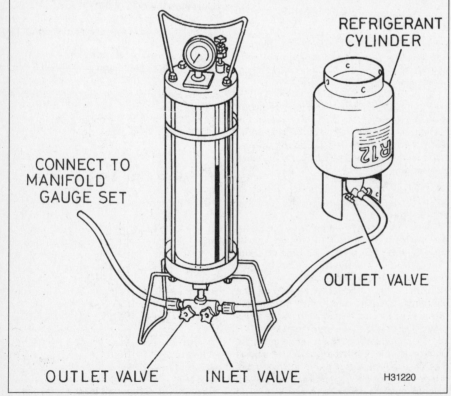

REFRIGERANT CYLINDER

CONNECT TO MANIFOLD GAUGE SET

OUTLET VALVE

OUTLET VALVE   INLET VALVE   H31220

Refrigerant cylinder (inverted to dispense liquid) connected to liquid charging cylinder

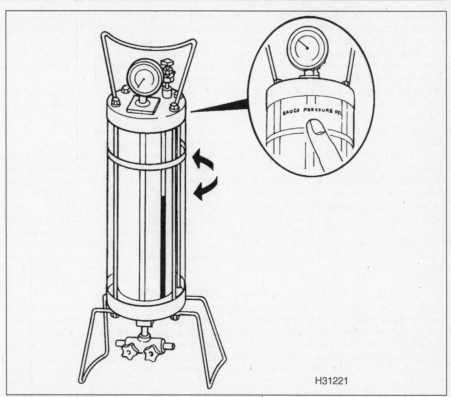

H31221

Rotate the graduated sleeve on the charging cylinder until the appropriate pressure scale on the graduated sleeve aligns with the sight glass tube

charging cylinder, then close the charging cylinder inlet valve. Always make sure that the recommended maximum level for the charging cylinder is not exceeded.

9 If the charging cylinder has a built-in heater, switch on the heater to warm the cylinder. If the charging cylinder does not have a built-in heater, fit it with an electric blanket type heater and switch on.

⚠ *Warning: Keep an eye on the charging cylinder pressure gauge to ensure that the maximum recommended pressure for the cylinder is not exceeded (the electric heater should cut out well before the maximum pressure is reached).*

10 Connect the manifold gauge set service (yellow) hose to the outlet valve on the charging cylinder.

11 Once the heater has been switched off, and the pressure inside the charging cylinder has stabilised (keep an eye on the pressure gauge), read off the pressure indicated on the charging cylinder pressure gauge.

12 Rotate the graduated sleeve on the charging cylinder until the appropriate pressure scale on the graduated sleeve aligns with the sight glass tube **(see illustration)**.

13 Check the level of liquid refrigerant in the sight glass, and read off the level on the scale **(see illustration)**. Again, check the amount of refrigerant required to charge the system (refer to the plate or label on the vehicle, or to the Specifications provided in Chapter 8).

Subtract the amount of refrigerant required to charge the system from the level of refrigerant indicated in the sight glass. The result will give the desired final reading in the sight glass to indicate that the system has been fully charged.

eg:

Initial reading in sight glass =
  1100 grams
Required refrigerant charge =
  950 grams
Desired final reading in sight glass =
  1100 – 950 = 150 grams

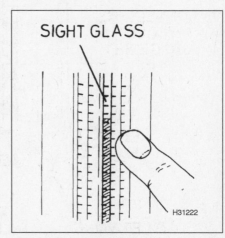

SIGHT GLASS

H31222

Read off the refrigerant level on the sight glass scale

6

Remember to make allowance for the fact that the hoses between the refrigerant cylinder and the service valve on the vehicle will have to be filled with refrigerant before any can enter the system. As a very rough guide it's probably wise to allow for approximately 30 g of refrigerant per metre of hose (ie, in addition to the recommended charge weight, for every metre of hose, add an extra 30 g of refrigerant). Note that this amount of refrigerant is often allowed for in the manufacturer's refrigerant charge specification tolerance. If the specified charge weight is unknown, always err on the low side – a system will operate with a low charge, but there is a risk of injury and damage to the system components if the system is overcharged.

14 Open the outlet valve on the charging cylinder, and if necessary carefully purge the air from the manifold gauge service hose, in accordance with the manufacturer's instructions.

15 Slowly open the high side (red) hand valve on the manifold gauge set, and allow refrigerant to enter the system until the refrigerant level in the charging cylinder sight glass falls to the desired level **(see illustration)**. When the refrigerant level in the charging cylinder sight glass reaches the desired level, close the high side (red) hand valve on the manifold gauge set.

16 Close the charging cylinder outlet valve, and if not already done, switch off the charging cylinder heater.

17 When charging is complete, disconnect the manifold gauge service hose from the refrigerant charging cylinder. Take care, as a small amount of refrigerant will be released as the hose is disconnected.

18 On completion, before disconnecting the manifold gauge set, check the system temperatures and pressures, and check the performance of the system, as described previously in *Preliminary work*.

19 Once the manifold gauge set has been disconnected, it's advisable to check for leaks around the system service valves – see *Leak testing*.

Leak testing

Refer to *Preliminary work* for details of leak testing when there is refrigerant in the system.

Refer to *Pressure testing a system* and *Evacuating a system* for details of leak testing when the system has been discharged.

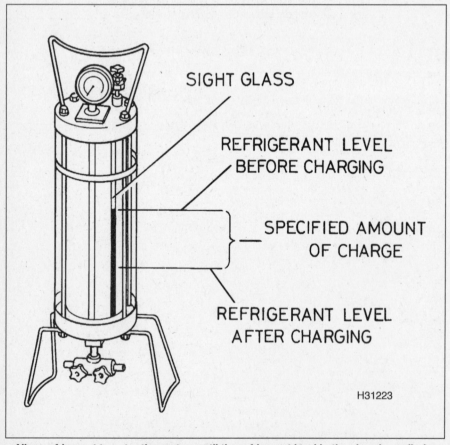

SIGHT GLASS

REFRIGERANT LEVEL BEFORE CHARGING

SPECIFIED AMOUNT OF CHARGE

REFRIGERANT LEVEL AFTER CHARGING

H31223

Allow refrigerant to enter the system until the refrigerant level in the charging cylinder sight glass falls to the desired level

Flushing system components

 Warning: Only the heat exchangers (condenser and evaporator) and the system pipework and hoses should be flushed. NEVER attempt to flush the other components (filter/drier, accumulator, orifice tube, expansion valve, and especially the compressor), as damage could be caused.

 Warning: Use only an air conditioning system flushing fluid for flushing work. DO NOT use refrigerant, water, air or any other fluids.

Flushing removes solid contaminants – excess oil, sludge, metallic debris from a failed compressor, etc, – which could cause poor cooling, or even component failure.

Flushing is essential when replacing a failed compressor. If the system components are not flushed, small particles of metal from the old compressor will remain in the system and eventually find their way into the new compressor, destroying it.

Excess compressor oil in the system can result in poor performance, and excessive amounts can even damage the compressor. Flushing will remove the oil.

Flushing procedure

Various manufacturers produce different types of flushing equipment, and the manufacturer's instructions should always be followed closely. The following procedure will act as a general guide when using basic equipment.

It is suggested that oxygen-free nitrogen (OFN) is used as a source of pressure during the flushing procedure because this will avoid the introduction of air (and hence moisture) into the system. It's possible to use compressed air as an alternative to OFN, but obviously this will introduce air and moisture into the component(s) being flushed (it should be possible to remove all the air and moisture if the system is evacuated for an extended period).

With the system discharged as described in *Discharging a system*, proceed as follows.

1 Disconnect the relevant refrigerant lines to allow access to the condenser, evaporator, or the appropriate pipework, as applicable.

2 Fill a flushing cylinder with suitable flushing fluid (follow the equipment manufacturer's instructions), then connect the outlet hose from the flushing cylinder to the inlet of the component to be flushed.

3 Connect a supply hose from an oxygen-free nitrogen (OFN) cylinder (or a compressed air supply), to the pressure connection on the flushing cylinder.

4 Connect another hose to the outlet of the component to be flushed, and place the end of the hose in a container (such as a bucket) to catch the waste flushing fluid **(see illustration)**.

5 Open the main valve on the OFN cylinder, then turn the regulator to give a suitable pressure (20 to 30 psi/138 to 207 kPa should be sufficient) on the regulator gauge.

 Warning: NEVER exceed the maximum recommended pressure for the flushing cylinder – check the manufacturer's information for details.

6 Where applicable, open the valve on the flushing cylinder, and allow the flushing fluid to flow through the relevant component into the waste container.

7 If necessary, reverse flush the component (flush the component in the opposite direction) to ensure that all debris is removed.

8 When flushing is complete, disconnect the flushing equipment, and dispose of the waste flushing fluid safely.

9 If the system components are to be left disconnected for any length of time, cover the open ends of the connections to prevent moisture and dirt entering the system.

10 When recharging the system with refrigerant and compressor oil, bear in mind that **all** the compressor oil will have been removed from any flushed components. Ensure that the appropriate amount of compressor oil is added to the relevant component(s) when refitting.

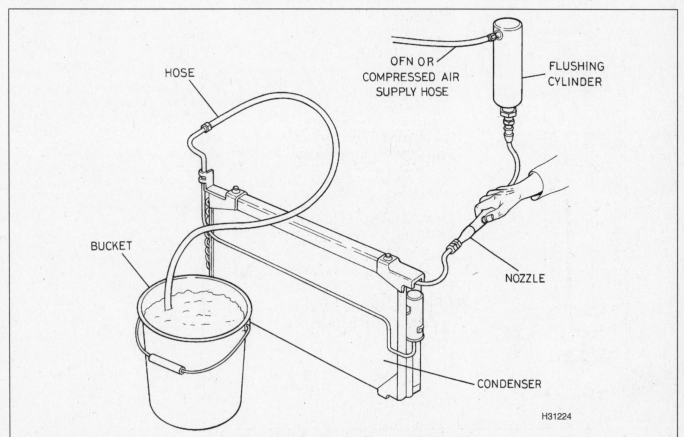

H31224

Flushing equipment connected to a condenser

6

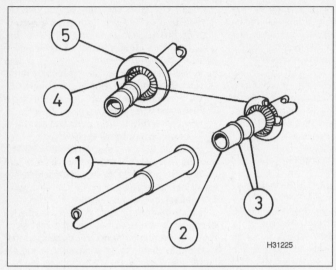

Spring-lock refrigerant line coupling components

1 Female fitting
2 Male fitting
3 O-rings
4 Garter spring
5 Cage

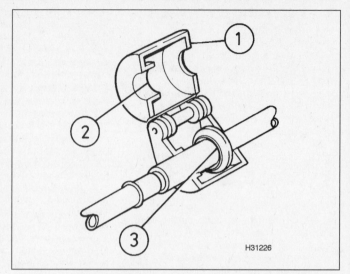

Fit the tool (1) over the spring-lock coupling with the projecting boss (2) against the open garter spring (3)

Basic repair procedures

Whenever any repair procedures are carried out, it's vital to observe scrupulous cleanliness. Always thoroughly clean around pipe and hose connections before disconnecting them, and plug or cover all open connections immediately to prevent the entry of dirt, air and moisture.

Always ensure that the system has been discharged before carrying out any repair work.

Once the system has been completely discharged, repairs can be performed. Some of the most common repairs include curing leaks, repairing or replacing hoses or pipes, renewing expansion valves, accumulators, filter/driers, condensers, and compressor reed valves.

Refrigerant line connections

Great care should always be taken when disconnecting and reconnecting refrigerant lines. Always use new O-rings when reconnecting refrigerant lines, and take care not to twist metal pipes, or overtighten union nuts.

Screw-fit connections

When disconnecting conventional screw-fit connections, always use two spanners, one to counterhold the connection and one to unscrew the union nut. This will prevent twisting of the refrigerant line, which may weaken the line, or may even cause the soft metal to fracture (a small fracture is not always obvious), causing leaks.

Disconnecting spring-lock couplings

Note: To disconnect a spring-lock coupling, an appropriate special tool will be required. Note that there are several different sizes of spring-lock coupling, and several corresponding sizes of special tool.

Before disconnecting a fitting, thoroughly clean the area on both sides of the connection to prevent any contamination from entering the system **(see illustration)**.

Use the appropriate tool to disconnect a coupling as follows.

1 Place the appropriate tool over the connection, with the projecting boss on the inside face of the tool against the open garter spring. Close the tool around the connection **(see illustration)**.

2 Push the tool along the pipe, so that the boss on the inside of the tool presses against the garter spring. Simultaneously, pull the two pipes apart to separate the coupling **(see illustrations)**.

3 Open the tool and remove it from the pipes. The coupling can now be fully separated.

4 It's advisable to renew the O-rings whenever the coupling is disconnected (see Renewing O-rings).

5 To reconnect the coupling, proceed as follows.

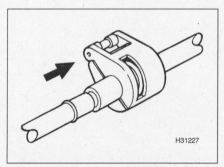

Push the tool so that the boss presses against the garter spring . . .

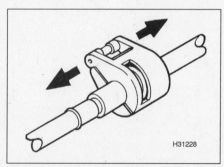

. . . and simultaneously pull the two pipes apart

6 Check the connection garter spring for obvious signs of damage, and fit a new spring if necessary.

7 Lightly lubricate the inner surfaces of the connection with clean compressor oil of the correct type and grade.

8 Push the two halves of the connection together with a slight twisting motion. Check that the connection is secure by ensuring that the garter spring has located over the flared end of the female fitting.

Curing leaks

Leaks are undoubtedly the most common problem associated with automotive air conditioning systems. Normal engine vibration can loosen fittings over time, and the hoses and metal pipes can crack as they deteriorate with age, allowing refrigerant to leak out. A system should always be leak tested when any work is carried out on it (see *Basic service procedures*).

Here's a quick guide to finding and curing leaks.

Loose fittings or connections

If a minor leak is traced to a connection, the fitting may have loosened due to vibration. Try tightening the connection. Always counterhold connections with a second spanner when tightening them, to avoid the risk of damage due to twisting. After tightening a connection or fitting, always check it again for leaks to make sure that the problem has been solved.

Take care not to overtighten unions, as overtightening can cause coupling flanges to crack **(see illustration)**.

Deteriorated O-rings or gaskets

If tightening a leaky connection doesn't stop the leak, the fitting O-ring seals or gaskets (as applicable) are probably deteriorated, although it's possible that the fitting itself is faulty or damaged.

Discharge the system and disconnect the fittings at the leaky connection. Be sure to clean the area around the fittings before disconnecting them, to prevent dirt from entering the system. Again, always use two spanners when loosening or tightening fittings to avoid the risk of damage due to twisting.

If the fittings appear to be in good condition, renewing the O-rings or gaskets (as applicable) will probably cure the problem. Always ensure that the O-rings or gaskets are compatible with the refrigerant (R12 or R134a) used in the system. Some O-rings/gaskets are compatible with both types of refrigerant, but some R12 O-rings/ gaskets cannot be used in R134a systems, and *vice versa*.

After renewing a seal or gasket, always carry out a leak test on the system before charging with refrigerant, to make sure that the leak has been cured. If the connection still leaks, it's likely that the connection itself is faulty or damaged. A new connection will have to be fitted, or the relevant hose or pipe will have to be renewed.

Porous, damaged or deteriorated hoses

If a leak is due to a defective hose, the hose will have to be renewed (see *Renewing hoses and metal pipes*).

Compressor seal leaks

If a leak is due to a compressor seal, the compressor must be overhauled or renewed. Due to the large number of different types of compressor in use, and because of the specialised tools required for compressor overhaul, compressor overhaul procedures are not covered in this book. It may be possible to exchange the old compressor for a new or reconditioned unit. For compressor overhaul details, refer to the vehicle or compressor manufacturer's information.

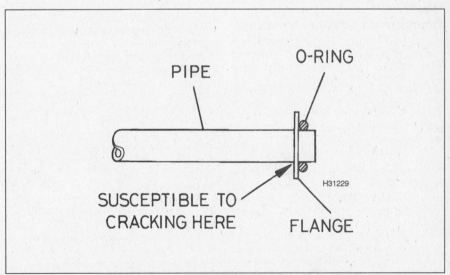

Overtightening of refrigerant pipe unions can cause cracking of the coupling flange

6

Component renewal

Although automotive air conditioning components differ in detail, the following information will provide a guide to the renewal of the various system components.

Whenever any component is renewed, or removed and refitted, new O-rings seals should always be fitted to the connection(s).

Note: *Whenever a component which contains compressor oil is renewed (such as a hose, pipe, condenser, evaporator, etc), the oil remaining inside the component will be lost from the system. It's important to ensure that a suitable quantity of compressor oil is added when recharging the system, to compensate for the oil lost – see Compressor oils.*

Renewing hose fittings

Note: Suitable crimping tools will be required to successfully fit new hose fittings and to provide a leak-free seal. Do not attempt to improvise crimping tools.

Before disconnecting a fitting, thoroughly clean the area on both sides of the connection to prevent any contamination from entering the system. Ensure that the system has been discharged, then proceed as follows.

1 Cut off the defective fitting with a sharp knife by cutting through the hose behind the fitting clamp. Keep the hose ends square. Discard the defective fitting and the end of the hose which has been cut off.

2 Check the end of the shortened hose for adequate flexibility; it must not be so short that it will be stretched taut when the engine moves under load, and when starting. In many cases, it will be necessary to fit a complete new hose.

3 When attaching a new fitting to a hose, if necessary lubricate the end of the hose and the fitting with clean compressor oil of the correct type and grade. Do not use any other kind of lubricant.

4 Work the fitting onto the end of the hose or with a twisting motion. This will help to seat the locating beads or barbs in the hose. Fittings must be completely seated before they are secured in place. If there's a locating shoulder on the fitting, push the fitting onto the end of the hose until the shoulder abuts the end of the hose.

5 Secure the fitting to the end of the hose using an appropriate crimping tool. Use only purpose-built tools for the type of connection being fitted. Do not attempt to improvise crimping tools.

Renewing hoses and metal pipes

Note: *When renewing hoses, always use the correct type of hose for the type of system being worked on. R134a systems use barrier hoses. Do not attempt to use anything except R134a hose for an R134a system, or refrigerant will escape through the walls of the hose.*

1 Before disconnecting a fitting, thoroughly clean the area on both sides of the connection to prevent any contamination from entering the system.

2 Always counterhold connections with a second spanner when loosening them, to avoid the risk of damage due to twisting.

3 Seal the ends of all hoses and pipes immediately after disconnecting them to prevent the entry of dirt, air and moisture.

4 Manufacturers usually remove moisture from, then cap, all replacement hoses and pipes. Do not remove the protective caps until hose or pipe is about to be fitted.

5 Metal pipes must be free from twists and kinks. Inspect new pipes before fitting to ensure that they are straight. Handle new pipes carefully to make sure that they are not damaged before fitting.

6 If the old pipes or hoses were supported by brackets, make sure that the new lines are positioned in the same brackets. If this is not done, the lines may be subjected to unnecessary strain and vibration, which could cause failure at a later date.

Renewing O-rings

When renewing O-rings, always ensure that the O-rings are compatible with the refrigerant (R12 or R134a) used in the system. Some O-rings are compatible with both types of refrigerant, but some R12 O-rings cannot be used in R134a systems, and *vice versa*.

Screw-fit connections

1 Disconnect the relevant pipe or hose connection (always counterhold connections with a second spanner when loosening them, to avoid the risk of damage due to twisting). After disconnecting a hose or pipe, plug the openings immediately to prevent the entry of dirt and moisture.

2 Remove and discard the old O-ring(s).

3 If it proves necessary to flush the refrigerant line(s), carry out flushing with flushing fluid (see *Flushing system components*). Never blow the lines through with an air line, as this will introduce air and possibly moisture into the system.

4 When fitting a new O-ring, make sure that the O-ring is butting up against the appropriate raised portion on the pipe.

5 Lubricate the area around the O-ring with compressor oil of the correct type and grade. Do not lubricate the joint threads with compressor oil.

6 Insert the tube into the fitting until the O-ring is no longer visible, then tighten the nut securely (again, counterhold with a second spanner to avoid damage).

7 Before charging the system with refrigerant, carry out a pressure test (see *Pressure testing a system*) to ensure that the connection is leak-free.

Spring-lock couplings

1 Disconnect the spring-lock coupling as described previously (see *Disconnecting spring-lock couplings*).

2 Carefully remove and discard the O-rings from the male pipe end.

3 If it proves necessary to flush the refrigerant line(s), carry out flushing with flushing fluid (see *Flushing system components*). Never blow the lines through with an air line, as this will introduce air and possibly moisture into the system.

4 When fitting new O-rings, make sure that the O-rings are correctly located in the slots in the pipe.

5 Reconnect the spring-lock coupling as described previously.

Condenser renewal

Various different types of condenser are available, but if possible, it's always preferable to use the manufacturer's approved replace-ment parts. Pattern and 'universal' replacement condensers are available from various sources, and these can be used provided that the appropriate size of condenser is used for the particular system in question. If a 'universal' replacement condenser is used, it may be necessary to modify the mountings and/or connections to enable it to fit.

Always take great care not to damage the condenser fins during removal and refitting.

Bear in mind that an air conditioning condenser is built to withstand the high pressures present in the high side of a system. Never be tempted to fit a cooling system radiator in place of a condenser, as aside from not being designed for air conditioning use, it will probably not cope with the high pressures.

Evaporator renewal

When renewing an evaporator, it will almost certainly be necessary to use the manufacturer's approved replacement part, due to the fact that the evaporator must fit inside the moulded heater/evaporator casing.

As with the condenser, take care not to damage the condenser fins during removal and refitting.

Filter/drier and accumulator renewal

Note: *If the filter/drier or accumulator is removed for any reason, always cap the refrigerant ports immediately to prevent the entry of moisture. Similarly, if a new filter/drier or accumulator is to be fitted, ensure that the new unit is supplied with seals fitted to the refrigerant ports – if no seals are fitted, refuse to accept the new unit, because the desiccant will almost certainly be saturated with moisture from the atmosphere.*

Filter/driers and accumulators may be sealed units, or it may be possible to dismantle them to enable renewal of the desiccant material.

The system filter/drier or accumulator should be renewed as a matter of course if the system has had a major refrigerant leak, or if the expansion valve or orifice tube has been renewed. It's advisable to renew the desiccant, or the complete unit, as applicable, whenever any major work (such as compressor or condenser renewal) is carried out on the system, if there is any suspicion that the desiccant is fully saturated, or if there is any evidence of moisture in the refrigerant when the system is discharged.

Ideally, the filter/drier or accumulator should be renewed annually, although the individual owner may decide against this on economic grounds if there is no evidence of excessive moisture in the system.

Filter/drier and accumulator desiccant renewal

On some vehicles, if the desiccant in the filter/drier or accumulator, as applicable, becomes saturated, allowing moisture to build up inside the system, it's possible to renew the desiccant without the need to renew the complete filter/drier or accumulator unit **(see illustration)**.

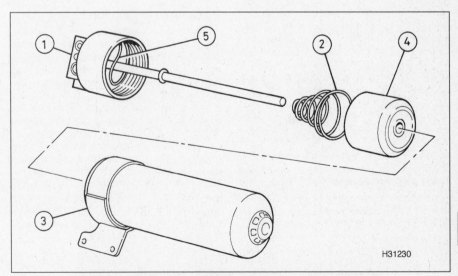

H31230

Typical filter/drier assembly with renewable desiccant cartridge

1 Upper section of filter/drier assembly   3 Filter/drier body
2 Spring   4 Desiccant cartridge

6

The system must always be discharged before carrying out this work.

Always follow the manufacturer's instructions when renewing the desiccant, and ensure that the correct type of replacement desiccant is used.

Expansion valve renewal

The expansion valve should be renewed if it is suspected of being faulty, and should always be renewed if the compressor has failed, or if the system is heavily contaminated.

If the expansion valve is to be renewed, always ensure that the replacement unit is similar to the original.

Whenever the expansion valve is renewed, it is advisable to renew the filter/drier.

Orifice tube renewal

An orifice tube is a relatively inexpensive component, and so it's good practise to renew it whenever the system is discharged for servicing. The orifice tube should also be renewed if the compressor has failed, or if the system is heavily contaminated.

If the orifice tube is to be renewed, always ensure that the replacement tube is similar to the original.

Always ensure that new O-rings are used when fitting a new orifice tube.

Whenever the orifice tube is renewed, it is advisable to renew the accumulator.

Orifice tubes are normally located in the evaporator inlet pipe, and a special removal tool will be required to remove the orifice tube from the pipe.

The following procedure is typical for the removal of most orifice tubes.

1 Discharge the air conditioning system.
2 Thoroughly clean the area on both sides of the evaporator inlet pipe connection to prevent any contamination from entering the system.
3 Unscrew the pipe connection, counter-holding the connection with a second spanner.
4 Engage the removal tool with the orifice tube, then turn the tool clockwise, to engage the lugs on the orifice tube.
5 Turn the nut on the top of the tool slowly clockwise to withdraw the orifice tube from the pipe. Take care, as it's possible to break the orifice tube during removal. If the tube breaks off during removal, a special tool will have to be obtained to extract the broken section.
6 Ensure that the new orifice tube is fitted with new O-rings, then lubricate the O-rings with a little clean compressor oil of the correct type.
7 Insert the new orifice tube into the evaporator inlet pipe, with the shorter end of the tube (orifice tubes are usually marked with a refrigerant flow direction arrow) towards the evaporator. Push the tube until it seats correctly in the pipe.
8 Reconnect and tighten the evaporator inlet pipe union, using a new O-ring where applicable (lubricate the new O-ring with a little clean compressor oil of the correct type).
9 Charge the air conditioning system with refrigerant, and check the system operation.

Compressor reed valve renewal

On most compressors, the reed valves can be renewed without major dismantling of the compressor. The valves are usually incorporated into a thin plate, similar to a gasket, which can be accessed by removing the rear cover from the compressor. Refer to the relevant compressor manufacturer's overhaul information for further details.

Compressor renewal

The compressor should be renewed if obvious heavy wear has taken place, or if the compressor is obviously seized or damaged (often indicated by the presence of small metal particles in the refrigerant, which are likely to cause a restriction in the refrigerant flow). Always ensure that the new compressor is of the same type as the original. Note that it may be possible to rebuild a compressor, or fit a reconditioned unit, but the cost of this should always be considered against the cost of a new component.

When the old compressor is removed, pour out and collect any remaining compressor oil, and ensure that the same quantity of fresh oil is added to the new compressor before fitting. If it is suspected that the compressor oil level was low, or if the system heat exchangers have been flushed, removing most of the oil from the system, add the full recommended quantity of oil to the new compressor (see *Compressor oils*).

Compressor overhaul

Compressor overhaul can be an involved and time-consuming process. If it appears that work other than reed valve renewal or compressor shaft seal renewal is required, the time and expense involved in carrying out the work should be considered against the cost of a new or reconditioned unit. The cost and availability of the necessary spare parts is also likely to rule out the possibility of overhaul.

If it is decided to proceed with compressor overhaul, ensure that the necessary spare parts are available, and either check that suitable manufacturer's overhaul information is available, or make precise notes during dismantling to ensure that the compressor is rebuilt correctly.

Chapter 7
Fault diagnosis

Contents

Introduction . . . . .7•1
Fault diagnosis sequence . . . . .7•3
   Normal air conditioning system operation . . . . .7•3
   Condenser cooling fan check . . . . .7•4
   Battery voltage . . . . .7•4
   Fault diagnosis procedures . . . . .7•4
Fault diagnosis flowcharts . . . . .7•4
   The system provides no cooling airflow . . . . .7•5
   The cool air output is inadequate . . . . .7•7
   The system provides intermittent cooling airflow . . . . .7•8

The system is noisy in operation . . . . .7•9
The compressor clutch does not engage . . . . .7•10
General fault diagnosis procedures . . . . .7•11
   General problems . . . . .7•11
   Compressor clutch coil checks . . . . .7•12
   Automatic air conditioning/climate control systems . . . . .7•13
Manifold gauge tests . . . . .7•14
   Normal manifold gauge readings .7•15
   Interpreting abnormal manifold gauge readings . . . . .7•16

Introduction

In the previous Chapters, we've discussed how an automotive air conditioning system works, and seen how to carry out basic servicing and repair work. However, now we've covered the basics, it's time to look at the diagnosis of specific problems.

It's quite likely that the reason you're working on an air conditioning system in the first place is because there's a problem. Knowledge is the most useful tool for fault diagnosis, and if you have a good understanding of the basic principles of air conditioning operation you'll have a head-start when it comes to solving problems.

The second most important fault diagnosis tool is the manifold (test) gauge set. Interpreting the readings obtained on manifold gauges is the key to fast and accurate fault diagnosis.

The most common causes of trouble with automotive air conditioning systems are:
1) Low refrigerant charge (leaks).
2) Blockages.
3) Electrical faults.

With any fault-finding, the first step is to decide where to begin investigations. Sometimes this is obvious, but more often than not, some detective work will be necessary. Always take into account any warning signs or abnormalities that may have been noticed in the period preceding the fault – unusual noises (compressor problems?), lack of cooling action, recent accident damage (condenser damage?), etc. – and bear in mind that the failure of components such as control system fuses or relays may only be pointers to some underlying fault.

The pages which follow should help to find the causes of the more common problems likely to afflict a vehicle air conditioning system. Whatever the fault, certain basic principles apply. These are as follows:
• **Verify the fault.** This is simply a matter of being sure that you know what the symptoms are before starting work. This is particularly important if you are investigating a fault for someone who may not have described it very clearly.

• **Don't overlook the obvious.** For example if the system does not operate at all, is the compressor drivebelt broken or missing, or is the air temperature too low for the ambient temperature sensor (where applicable) or the lower pressure cut-out switch to allow the system to operate? Many problems are caused by electrical faults (poor connections or breaks in wiring), so check for loose or broken wiring before digging out the test equipment.

• **Cure the disease, not the symptom.** Charging a system which is low on refrigerant will get the system working in the short-term, but the problem will soon re-appear if the low refrigerant level was due to a leak (and you'll be responsible for venting refrigerant into the atmosphere!).

• **Don't take anything for granted.** Particularly, don't forget that a new component may itself be defective. Don't leave components out of a fault diagnosis procedure just because they are new or have been recently fitted.

7

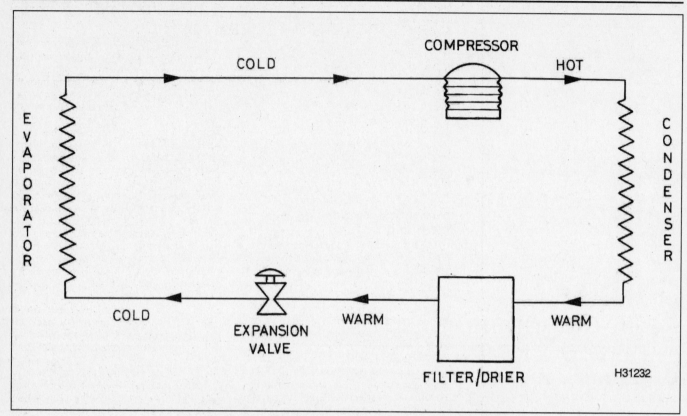

Normal refrigerant pipe temperatures for an expansion valve system

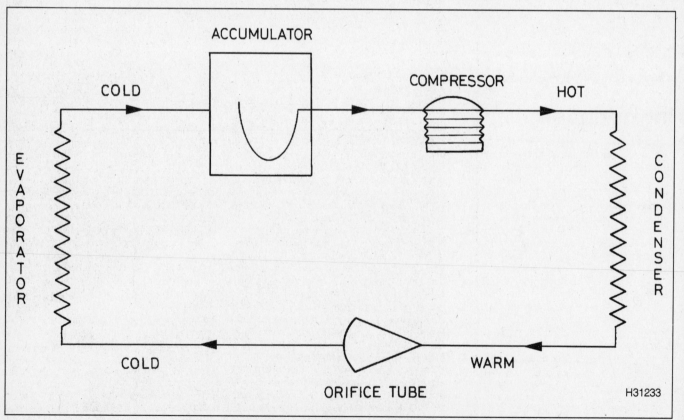

Normal refrigerant pipe temperatures for an orifice tube system

Fault diagnosis sequence

In order to trace a fault, it is important to follow a logical diagnostic procedure. This will make sure that obvious simple faults are not overlooked, and should avoid unnecessary diagnosis work on areas of the system which are working correctly.

First of all, it's helpful to know what to expect if the system is operating normally, you'll then be able to tell if there's a problem in the system, and you should be able to work out where to start looking for the source of trouble.

Normal air conditioning system operation

The temperatures of the refrigerant pipes in an air conditioning system can give a good indication as to whether the system is operating normally. When the air conditioning system is operating normally, the temperatures of the refrigerant pipes should be as follows (see illustrations opposite):

a) The pipe between the evaporator and the compressor will be cold.
b) The pipe between the compressor and the condenser will be hot.
c) The pipe between the condenser, and the expansion valve or orifice tube will be warm.
d) The pipe (where applicable) between the expansion valve or orifice tube, and the evaporator will be cold (take precautions against possible ice burns).

When the system is running with the temperature and blower motor controls set to maximum cooling, the air emerging from the vents in the passenger compartment should drop to a temperature between 10 and 15°C below the ambient temperature, and the temperature should rise and fall slightly as the compressor cycles. On a system with a cycling compressor, when the compressor clutch is heard to disengage, the temperature should start to rise slightly, and the temperature should start to fall again after the compressor cuts back in. The temperature of the air emerging from the vents can be checked with a simple, accurate thermometer (see illustration).

Remember that the airflow through the condenser has a significant effect on the operation of the system, so a fault may show up when the vehicle is being driven, but may not be obvious when the vehicle is stationary. For example, moisture inside the system is more likely to freeze when the vehicle is moving than when the vehicle is standing still (without the cooling airflow through the condenser, the system temperatures may not be low enough to allow the moisture to freeze). Similarly, a system which is low on refrigerant may operate normally when the vehicle is stationary, but may not provide sufficient cooling when the vehicle is moving.

The temperature of the air emerging from the vents can be checked with an accurate thermometer

Condenser cooling fan check

If a fault in the system is suspected, always begin the fault diagnosis procedure by checking the operation of the condenser cooling fan (see *Basic service procedures* in Chapter 6). Cooling fan faults can easily lead to engine overheating, and excessive condenser temperatures (which will in turn lead to excessive air conditioning system high side pressure, which may operate the compressor high pressure cut-out switch), especially when the vehicle is standing still.

Cure any problems before carrying out any further fault diagnosis work.

Battery voltage

On a system which is electronically controlled via an air conditioning electronic control unit (ECU), or using signals from an engine management ECU, before assuming that there is a problem with the air conditioning system, check the battery voltage. Even a problem as simple as a slack alternator drivebelt can result in low battery voltage, which can cause numerous problems (often intermittent problems) in electronic control systems.

Fault diagnosis procedures

It's suggested that the initial starting point for any fault diagnosis work should be to read through the flowcharts. This will establish whether or not the problem does actually lie in the air conditioning system, and will show the path to follow to find the cause of the trouble.

After the fault diagnosis charts, the section on *General fault diagnosis procedures* provides details of how to diagnose straightforward general problems not included in the flowcharts, details of how to check the compressor clutch coil, and brief details of fault diagnosis for automatic climate control systems.

The last section in this Chapter provides details of fault diagnosis using a manifold (test) gauge set, which will allow more detailed investigation and diagnosis of the air conditioning system operation.

Fault diagnosis flowcharts

If an air conditioning system appears not to work at all, this is probably one of the more straightforward problems to diagnose. Bear in mind that the problem may not be due to a fault in the air conditioning system; always check for obvious problems first, such as faults with the heater/ventilation/air conditioning controls and the air distribution system inside the vehicle.

The following flow charts should help to steer you along a logical path of diagnosis.

Chart 1: The system provides no cooling airflow

Heater/ventilation system component checks

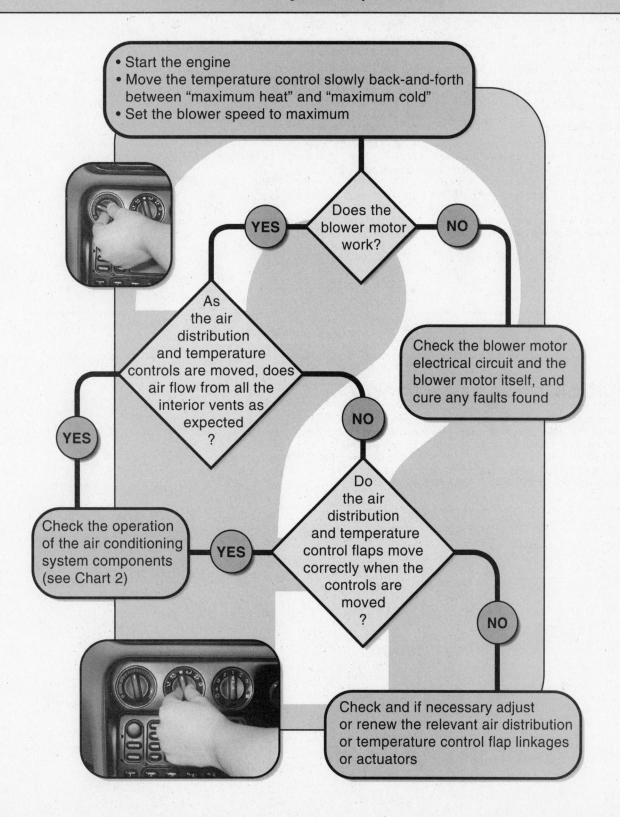

• Start the engine
• Move the temperature control slowly back-and-forth between "maximum heat" and "maximum cold"
• Set the blower speed to maximum

Does the blower motor work?

YES

NO

As the air distribution and temperature controls are moved, does air flow from all the interior vents as expected?

Check the blower motor electrical circuit and the blower motor itself, and cure any faults found

NO

YES

NO

Check the operation of the air conditioning system components (see Chart 2)

Do the air distribution and temperature control flaps move correctly when the controls are moved?

YES

NO

Check and if necessary adjust or renew the relevant air distribution or temperature control flap linkages or actuators

7

Chart 2: The system provides no cooling airflow

Air conditioning system component checks

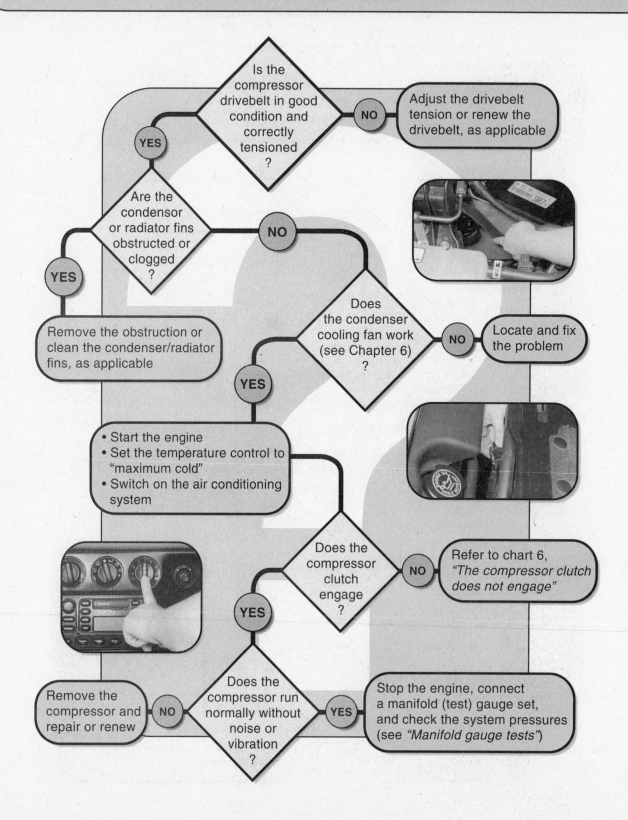

Is the compressor drivebelt in good condition and correctly tensioned ?

NO → Adjust the drivebelt tension or renew the drivebelt, as applicable

YES ↓

Are the condensor or radiator fins obstructed or clogged ?

NO →

YES ↓

Remove the obstruction or clean the condenser/radiator fins, as applicable

Does the condenser cooling fan work (see Chapter 6) ?

NO → Locate and fix the problem

YES ↓

• Start the engine
• Set the temperature control to "maximum cold"
• Switch on the air conditioning system

Does the compressor clutch engage ?

NO → Refer to chart 6, *"The compressor clutch does not engage"*

YES ↓

Does the compressor run normally without noise or vibration ?

YES → Stop the engine, connect a manifold (test) gauge set, and check the system pressures (see *"Manifold gauge tests"*)

NO → Remove the compressor and repair or renew

Chart 3: The cool air output is inadequate

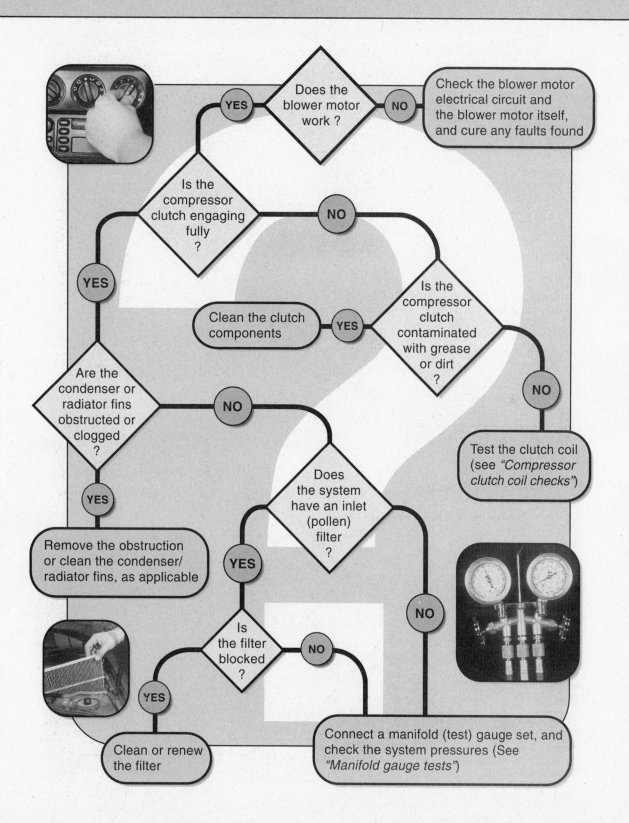

Does the blower motor work ?

YES

NO → Check the blower motor electrical circuit and the blower motor itself, and cure any faults found

Is the compressor clutch engaging fully ?

NO → **Is the compressor clutch contaminated with grease or dirt ?**

YES → Clean the clutch components

NO → Test the clutch coil (see "Compressor clutch coil checks")

YES

Are the condenser or radiator fins obstructed or clogged ?

NO → **Does the system have an inlet (pollen) filter ?**

YES → Remove the obstruction or clean the condenser/radiator fins, as applicable

YES → **Is the filter blocked ?**

NO

YES → Clean or renew the filter

NO → Connect a manifold (test) gauge set, and check the system pressures (See "Manifold gauge tests")

Chart 4: The system provides intermittent cooling airflow

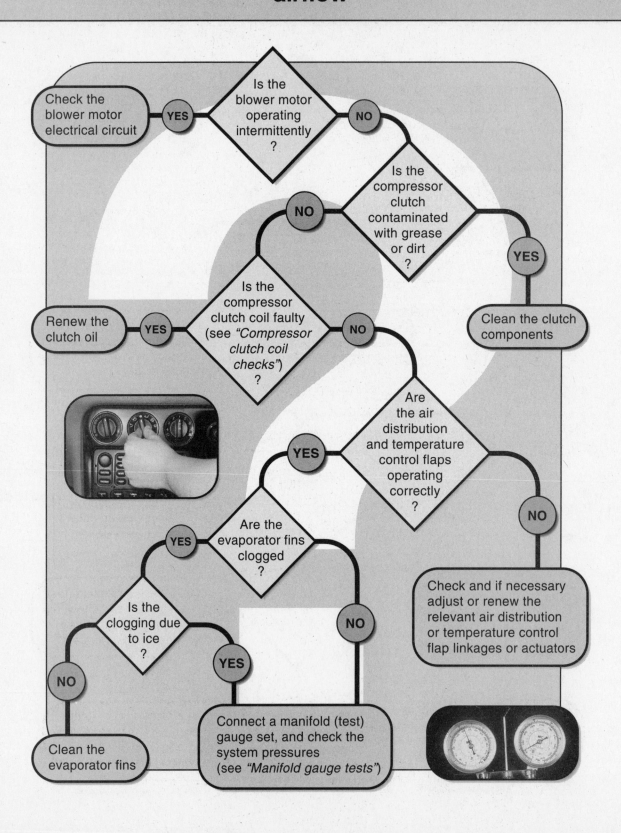

Is the blower motor operating intermittently?

YES → Check the blower motor electrical circuit

NO →

Is the compressor clutch contaminated with grease or dirt?

NO →

Is the compressor clutch coil faulty (see *"Compressor clutch coil checks"*)?

YES → Renew the clutch oil

NO →

YES → Clean the clutch components

Are the air distribution and temperature control flaps operating correctly?

YES →

Are the evaporator fins clogged?

YES →

Is the clogging due to ice?

NO → Clean the evaporator fins

YES →

NO →

Connect a manifold (test) gauge set, and check the system pressures (see *"Manifold gauge tests"*)

NO → Check and if necessary adjust or renew the relevant air distribution or temperature control flap linkages or actuators

Chart 5: The system is noisy in operation

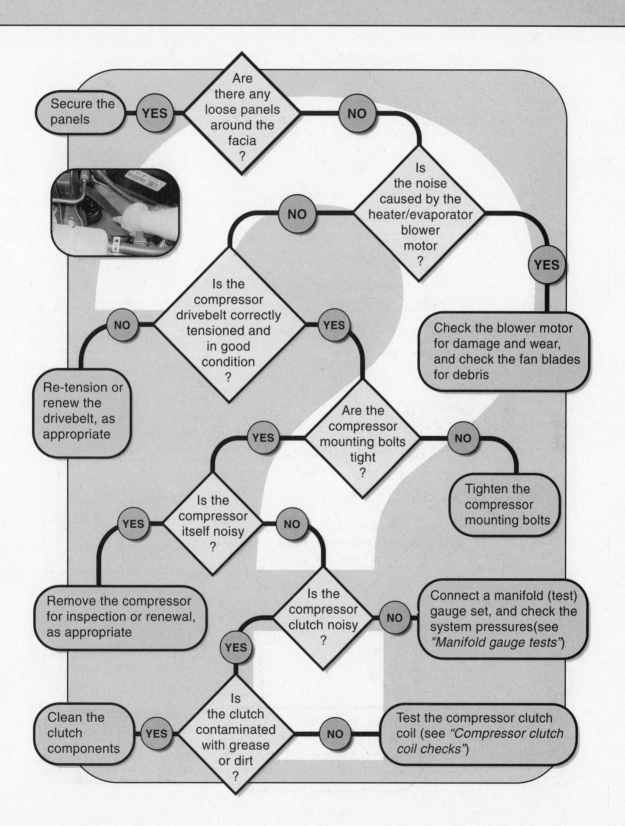

Are there any loose panels around the facia ?

YES → Secure the panels

NO → **Is the noise caused by the heater/evaporator blower motor ?**

YES → Check the blower motor for damage and wear, and check the fan blades for debris

NO → **Is the compressor drivebelt correctly tensioned and in good condition ?**

NO → Re-tension or renew the drivebelt, as appropriate

YES → **Are the compressor mounting bolts tight ?**

NO → Tighten the compressor mounting bolts

YES → **Is the compressor itself noisy ?**

YES → Remove the compressor for inspection or renewal, as appropriate

NO → **Is the compressor clutch noisy ?**

NO → Connect a manifold (test) gauge set, and check the system pressures(see *"Manifold gauge tests"*)

YES → **Is the clutch contaminated with grease or dirt ?**

YES → Clean the clutch components

NO → Test the compressor clutch coil (see *"Compressor clutch coil checks"*)

Chart 6: The compressor clutch does not engage

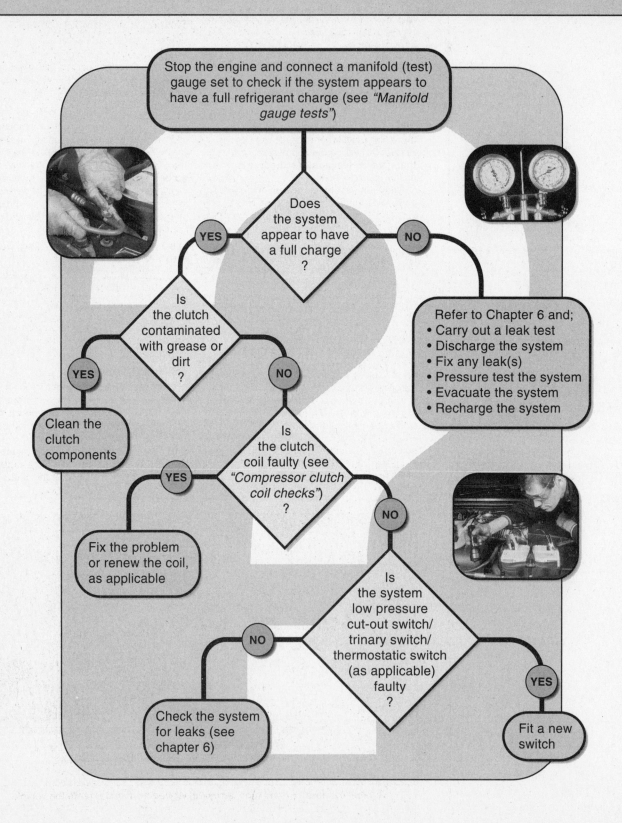

Stop the engine and connect a manifold (test) gauge set to check if the system appears to have a full refrigerant charge (see *"Manifold gauge tests"*)

Does the system appear to have a full charge ?

YES

NO

Refer to Chapter 6 and;
- Carry out a leak test
- Discharge the system
- Fix any leak(s)
- Pressure test the system
- Evacuate the system
- Recharge the system

Is the clutch contaminated with grease or dirt ?

YES

Clean the clutch components

NO

Is the clutch coil faulty (see *"Compressor clutch coil checks"*) ?

YES

Fix the problem or renew the coil, as applicable

NO

Is the system low pressure cut-out switch/ trinary switch/ thermostatic switch (as applicable) faulty ?

NO

Check the system for leaks (see chapter 6)

YES

Fit a new switch

General fault diagnosis procedures

This Section provides details of how to diagnose straightforward general problems not included in the flowcharts, details of how to check the compressor clutch coil, and brief details of fault diagnosis for automatic climate control systems.

General problems

Ice

If ice is present on any of the system components, this indicates that there is a restriction to the refrigerant flow at the particular point where the ice has formed. A restriction will cause a pressure drop, and therefore a temperature drop, which will enable ice to form.

Common problem areas include the condenser outlet line, filter/drier (expansion valve type systems) and the evaporator. If ice forms on one of the refrigerant lines, the restriction or blockage will be located at the precise point where the ice has formed. Note that moisture can also freeze on the outside of the evaporator, which will block the fins and prevent airflow through the evaporator, resulting in no (or reduced) cooling airflow inside the vehicle.

Smells

After a period of time, the moisture around the evaporator water drain may cause a build-up of mould and bacteria, causing an un-pleasant odour when the system is operating.

The problem can be cured by spraying a proprietary cleaner/disinfectant around the bottom of the evaporator.

Access to the evaporator can be tricky on some vehicles, unless major dismantling work is carried out. To overcome this problem, a small hole can be drilled in the heater casing under the evaporator, and the cleaner can be sprayed in through a small tube. Make sure that the hole is drilled in exactly the right place to avoid damage.

Sloshing noise around corners

This will almost certainly be due to a blocked evaporator drain causing a build-up of water under the evaporator. To cure the problem, simply unblock the evaporator drain tube(s) **(see illustration)**.

Windows inside vehicle mist up

If the inside surfaces of the windows mist up when the air conditioning system is switched on, or fail to clear when the system is switched on, it's likely that the evaporator water drain tube is blocked. Because the condensation produced on the surface of the evaporator cannot escape, the moisture remains in the air inside the vehicle and forms as condensation on the windows.

System appears to be working, but warm air is delivered

If the air conditioning system appears to be operating normally, but only warm air is delivered through the vents inside the car, it's likely that the air mixing flaps between the heater matrix and evaporator are faulty. This applies particularly to models fitted with climate control systems.

Water under vehicle

On a vehicle equipped with air conditioning, it's normal to find water dripping from under the evaporator drain, particularly on a hot day. This is due to condensation forming on the outer surfaces of the evaporator. On a particularly warm day, the evaporator condensation can produce a large puddle of water under the vehicle, and this should not be mistaken for a coolant leak.

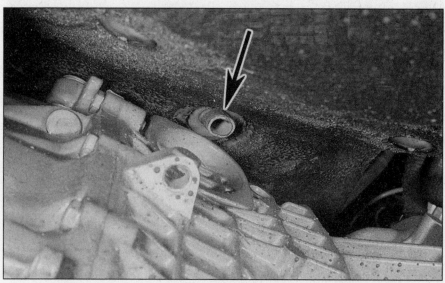

Typical evaporator drain tube (arrowed) viewed from underneath the vehicle

7

System operates when first switched on, then stops shortly afterwards

This problem is likely to be due to air in the system. The air will contain moisture, which may not cause a problem when the system is first switched on (although high system pressures may possibly be noticed), but may freeze, causing a blockage when the system has been running for a while.

Compressor clutch coil checks

If the compressor clutch coil is faulty, the vehicle engine will not be able to drive the compressor, and the air conditioning system will not work.

The following problems with the coil could prevent the clutch from working:

a) *No power to the clutch coil.*
b) *Poor earthing of clutch coil.*
c) *Incorrect coil resistance.*
d) *Incorrect clutch air gap.*

Checking for power to the clutch coil

If available, the vehicle wiring diagram will be a great help to the fault-finding process.

Start the engine and switch on the air conditioning then, using a multimeter, check for a 12-volt supply at the clutch coil supply terminal. If no supply is present, first check the main air conditioning on/off switch and any fuses or relays in the circuit.

Secondly, check the state of the system high pressure and low pressure cut-out switches (and/or any other compressor control components – see Chapter 2) – both should be closed (this can be checked using a multimeter or a continuity tester). If the low pressure cut-out switch is open, this probably means that the refrigerant charge is low (due to a leak). If the high pressure cut-out switch is open, this implies that the system has been overcharged, or the ambient or system temperature is excessive. Bear in mind though, that one or both pressure cut-out switches may be faulty.

If no faults are found, work back through the circuit, starting at the coil, and check for any breaks in the circuit wiring.

Repair any faults found, then re-check the circuit.

Checking the clutch coil earth

On many vehicles, the clutch coil is earthed through the vehicle engine, via the compressor body.

Using a multimeter, check the coil earth circuit.

Check the earth circuit, noting that dirty connections are a common source of problems.

Checking the clutch coil resistance

If power is reaching the coil, and there's a good earth circuit, but the clutch still doesn't engage, the problem is likely to be in the coil itself.

Beware of checking the coil continuity, as if continuity is present, it does not necessarily follow that the coil is working correctly. To check the coil conclusively, its resistance should be measured using a multimeter or ohmmeter. Generally speaking, the coil resistance should be close to one of the values in the table below.

If the coil resistance is not close to the expected figure, renew the coil.

Checking clutch coil air gap

In order for the compressor clutch to operate effectively, the air gap between the pulley and the driveplate must be within the specified limits (typically around 0.5 to 1.5 mm). If the air gap is too large, the magnetic field produced by the coil will not be able to pull the driveplate into engagement with the pulley.

On some compressors, the air gap can be adjusted by using packing shims, but in some cases, it may be necessary to renew the driveplate if the air gap is excessive. If the clutch face of the pulley is excessively worn or damaged, it may be possible to have it machined, otherwise, the pulley will have to be removed. Refer to the manufacturer's information for specific details.

Electrical system type	Coil resistance
Vehicles with 12-volt electrical system	Approximately 3 ohms
Vehicles with 24-volt electrical system	Approximately 14 ohms

Code	Significance
12	Start of fault code sequence
13 – 14	Air distribution flap position sensor
15 – 16	Air recirculation flap position sensor
17	Air distribution flap movement
18	Air mixer flap movement
21 – 22	Air mixer flap position sensor
23 – 24	Evaporator temperature sensor
25 – 26	Outside air temperature sensor
27	Air recirculation flap movement
31 – 32	Passenger compartment temperature sensor
35 – 36	Air mixer flap motor
46	Compressor control
51 – 52	Air inlet flap motor
53 – 54	Air distribution flap motor
55 – 56	Coolant temperature sensor
63 – 64	Blower motor and module
11	End of sequence

Automatic air conditioning/ climate control systems

In recent years, an increasing number of vehicles have been fitted with an electronically-controlled climate control system. Many of these systems incorporate a self-diagnostic system which stores details of any system faults as fault codes in the system electronic control unit (ECU) memory, or in some cases in the engine management electronic control unit (ECU) memory.

Fault codes can usually be read using an appropriate fault code reader **(see illustration)**, but always follow the equipment manufacturer's recommendations to avoid the risk of any damage to the electrical circuits.

The table (above) shows a typical example of the fault codes and their significance for the climate control system fitted to certain Peugeot 605 models. On this particular vehicle, the fault codes are stored in the climate control system electronic control unit.

Typical fault code reader

7

Manifold gauge tests

The manifold gauge set is without question the most important tool used when carrying out fault diagnosis on a vehicle air conditioning system. Manifold gauges allow the system high side and low side pressures to be measured, which is essential information for determining whether the system is operating correctly, and for fault diagnosis. For a full description of the manifold gauge set, refer to Chapter 4.

Interpreting the readings shown on a manifold gauge set is the key to accurate fault diagnosis. Once the gauge set has been connected to the system, a large number of internal system problems can be diagnosed **(see illustration)**.

The following pages provide typical examples of the readings likely to be obtained on manifold gauges due to a number of common problems which may need to be diagnosed.

Before proceeding, read the safety precautions given in Chapter 5.

Connect a manifold gauge set to the system as described in Chapter 6 (*Connecting a manifold (test) gauge set*).

Note: *The actual gauge readings shown in the following examples are typical, and varying equipment and ambient conditions may cause the actual values for the gauge readings to be different from those shown in the following pages. However, the relationship between the high and low side readings should be similar to the examples shown regardless of ambient conditions.*

Refer to the pressure/temperature relationship charts given in Chapter 6 (*Connecting a manifold (test) gauge set*) for a guide as to how the system pressures will vary according to temperature.

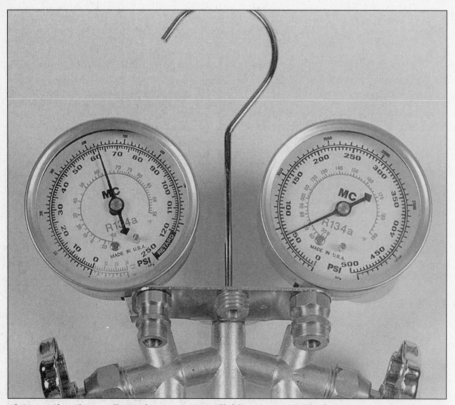

Interpreting the readings shown on a manifold gauge set is the key to accurate system fault diagnosis

Normal manifold gauge readings

If the system is operating normally, the high and low side pressures should always be the same when the system is switched off.

Typical pressures and temperatures for a system which is switched on and operating normally on a warm spring day would be:

Low side   35 psi (241 kPa)   4°C (39°F)
High side 180 psi (1241 kPa)   54°C (129°F)

The following gauge readings can be expected for a system which is operating normally, with no faults.

Air conditioning system switched off

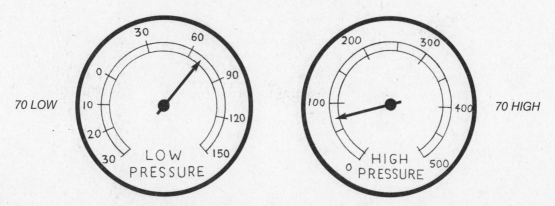

Gauge readings	Symptoms	Diagnosis
Low side pressure normal. High side pressure normal.	● Discharge air cold. ● Sight glass (where applicable) clear.	● System is functioning normally, and 'appears' to have a full refrigerant charge (not conclusive proof).

Air conditioning system switched on

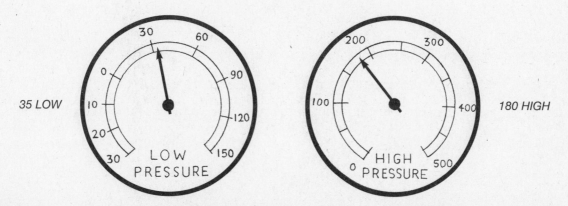

Gauge readings	Symptoms	Diagnosis
Low side pressure normal. High side pressure normal.	● Discharge air cold. ● Sight glass (where applicable) clear.	● System is functioning normally, and has a full refrigerant charge.

7

Interpreting abnormal manifold gauge readings

The following pages give typical examples of gauge readings which may indicate a fault in the system. For each set of gauge readings, a list of possible additional symptoms and an interpretation of the readings is provided in order to help to diagnose the cause of the problem.

Air conditioning system switched off

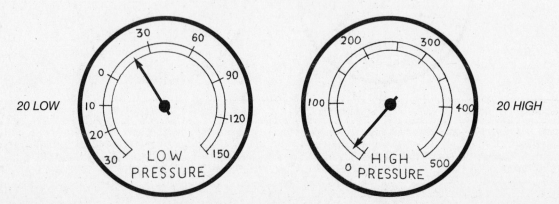

Gauge readings	Symptoms	Diagnosis
Low side pressure low. High side pressure low.	● The compressor will not run.	● Low refrigerant charge.

Air conditioning system switched on

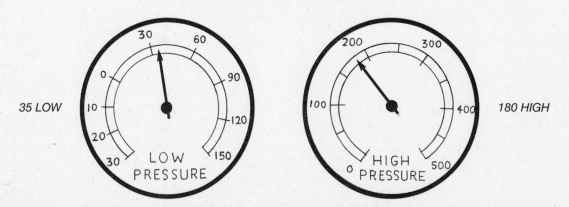

Gauge readings	Symptoms	Diagnosis
Low side pressure normal. High side pressure normal.	● Sight glass (where applicable) clear, or a few bubbles. ● Cool air discharged for a few minutes, then discharge air temperature rises. ● Low side gauge does not fluctuate as compressor cycles on and off.	● Air and moisture in the system (moisture is freezing, causing minor restriction in system).

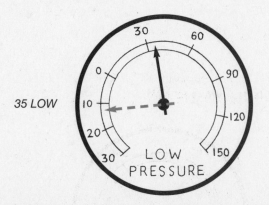

35 LOW

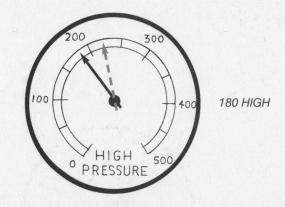

180 HIGH

Gauge readings	Symptoms	Diagnosis
Low side pressure normal-to-low, then moves into vacuum. High side pressure normal (may rise as low side moves into vacuum).	● Sight glass (where applicable) full of small bubbles. ● Cool air discharged for a few minutes, then discharge air temperature rises as low side moves into vacuum.	● Excessive air and moisture in the system (moisture is freezing and causing total blockage in system.

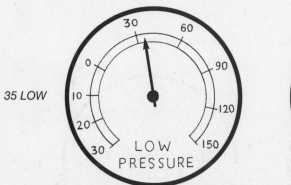

35 LOW

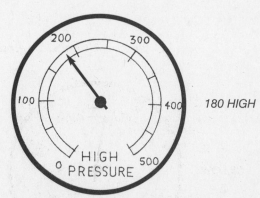

180 HIGH

Gauge readings	Symptoms	Diagnosis
Low side normal. High side normal.	● Compressor cycles on and off too quickly. ● Low side gauge does not indicate sufficient range.	● Faulty or incorrectly adjusted thermostatic switch, or pressure-sensitive (cycling) switch, as applicable (causing compressor to shut off too quickly).

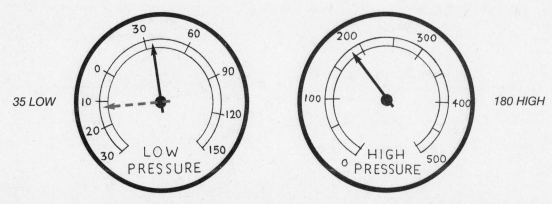

35 LOW — *180 HIGH*

Gauge readings	Symptoms	Diagnosis
Low side low-to-normal, or normal-to-high. High side normal.	● Lack of cooling air, or fluctuating amount of cooling air. ● Compressor cycles at incorrect pressure or temperature.	● Faulty or incorrectly adjusted thermostatic switch, or faulty low pressure cut-out switch, as applicable (causing the compressor to operate for too long, resulting in freezing at the evaporator – the freezing restricts the airflow through the evaporator fins, and the refrigerant flow through the evaporator passages).

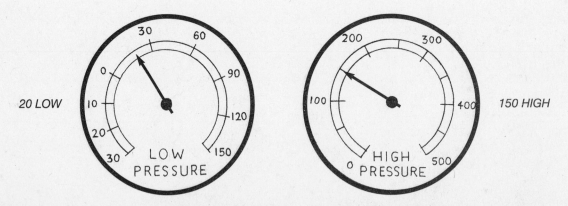

20 LOW — *150 HIGH*

Gauge readings	Symptoms	Diagnosis
Low side pressure low High side pressure low	● Discharge air only slightly cool ● Sight glass (where applicable) contains some bubbles.	● Refrigerant charge slightly low.

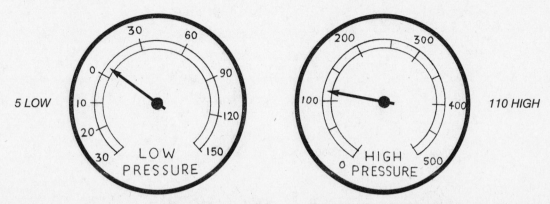

Gauge readings	Symptoms	Diagnosis
Low side pressure low High side pressure low	● Discharge air warm ● Compressor may stop	● Refrigerant charge very low (compressor may stop due to activation of low pressure cut-out switch).

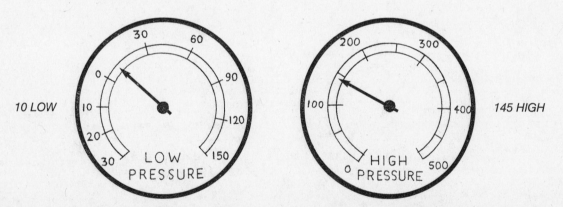

Gauge readings	Symptoms	Diagnosis
Low side pressure low. High side pressure low.	● Discharge air only slightly cool. ● Moisture or frost build-up on expansion valve.	● Expansion valve stuck closed (possibly due to blocked filter screen or faulty temperature sensing bulb), causing restriction of refrigerant flow.

7

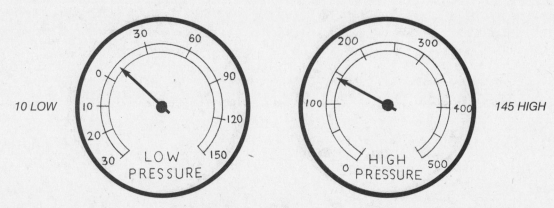

Gauge readings	Symptoms	Diagnosis
Low side pressure low. High side pressure low (may be normal-to-high if restriction is located immediately after the service valves).	● Discharge air only slightly cool. ● Moisture or frost on high side refrigerant lines.	● Restriction in high side of system (frost will build up immediately after the restriction).

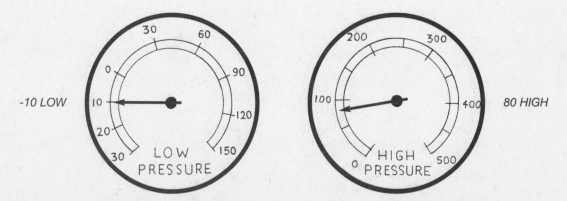

Gauge readings	Symptoms	Diagnosis
Low side pressure zero-to-negative. High side pressure low.	● Discharge air only slightly cool. ● Frost build-up on high side refrigerant lines (from filter/drier to evaporator).	● Refrigerant flow obstructed by dirt ● Blocked filter/drier.

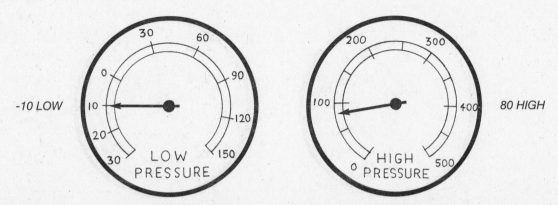

Gauge readings	Symptoms	Diagnosis
Low side pressure zero-to-negative. High side pressure low.	● Discharge air only slightly cool. ● Frost build-up on high side refrigerant lines (before and after filter/drier).	● Refrigerant flow obstructed by dirt or moisture (ice). ● Refrigerant flow obstructed by gas leakage from expansion valve temperature sensing bulb/capillary tube.

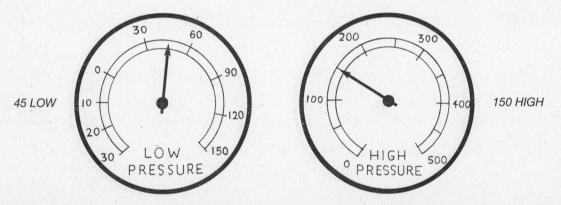

Gauge readings	Symptoms	Diagnosis
Low side pressure high. High side pressure low	● Noisy compressor.	● Loose or worn compressor drivebelt. ● Faulty compressor reed valve. ● Compressor internal fault.

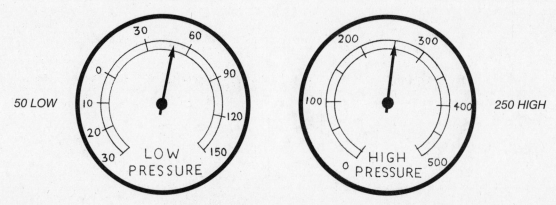

Gauge readings	Symptoms	Diagnosis
Low side pressure high. High side pressure high.	● Discharge air warm. ● High side refrigerant lines hot. ● Possibly, bubbles in sight glass (where applicable).	● Restricted or blocked condenser fins. ● Refrigerant overcharge. ● Faulty condenser cooling fan. ● Engine overheating. ● Air in system. ● Incorrect refrigerant in system.

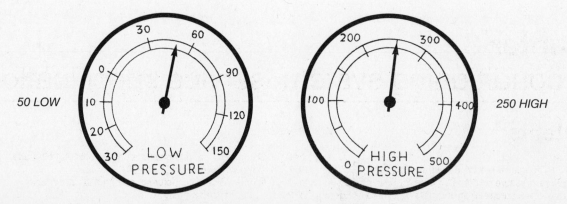

Gauge readings	Symptoms	Diagnosis
Low side pressure high. High side pressure high.	● Discharge air warm. ● Moisture or frost on evaporator and/or low side refrigerant lines.	● Expansion valve stuck open allowing excessive amounts of refrigerant through evaporator.

Chapter 8
Air conditioning system service specifications

Contents

Introduction . . . . .8•1
Refrigerant temperature/pressure relationships . . . . .8•2
   Temperature/pressure relationship data for R12 refrigerant . . .8•2
   Temperature/pressure relationship data for R134a refrigerant .8•2
Vehicle manufacturers' refrigerant and compressor oil
   recommendations . . . . .8•3

Compressor manufacturers' compressor PAG oil grade
   recommendations . . . . .8•4
Compressor manufacturers' compressor oil capacity
   recommendations . . . . .8•5
   Compressor mineral oil capacities for R12 systems . . . . .8•5
   Compressor PAG oil capacities for R134a systems . . . . .8•5

Introduction

The following pages list details of refrigerant temperature/pressure relationships, and give examples of refrigerant and compressor oil specifications for most UK model passenger cars and light commercial vehicles available since the early 1980s.

The compressor oil quantities given are for a complete air conditioning system when filled from dry (ie, with no residual compressor oil remaining in the system).

Vehicles fitted with air conditioning often have a system specifications plate or label, which can usually be found in the engine compartment, or on the compressor. In this case, always use the specification(s) given on the plate or label.

It's possible that some vehicles built in the late 1980s and early 1990s may have been converted from R12 systems to R134a systems, and specifications for these converted systems are not included in this Chapter.

8

Refrigerant temperature/pressure relationships

The following charts provide details of the relationship between temperature and pressure for R12 and R134a refrigerants. This information can be used to help identify refrigerants – see *Preliminary work* in Chapter 6.

Temperature/pressure relationship data for R12 refrigerant

Temperature °C (°F)	Pressure psi (kPa)
−20 (−4.0)	6.4 (44)
−18 (−0.4)	8.1 (56)
−16 (3.2)	10 (69)
−14 (6.8)	12 (83)
−12 (10.4)	15 (103)
−10 (14.0)	17 (117)
−8 (17.6)	19 (131)
−6 (21.2)	22 (152)
−4 (24.8)	24 (165)
−2 (28.4)	27 (186)
0 (32.0)	30 (207)
1 (33.8)	31 (214)
2 (35.6)	32 (221)
3 (37.4)	34 (234)
4 (39.2)	36 (248)
5 (41.0)	37 (255)
6 (42.8)	39 (269)
7 (44.6)	41 (283)
8 (46.4)	42 (290)
9 (48.2)	44 (303)
10 (50.0)	47 (324)
11 (51.8)	48 (331)
12 (53.6)	50 (345)
13 (55.4)	52 (359)
14 (57.2)	54 (372)
15 (59.0)	56 (386)
16 (60.8)	58 (400)
17 (62.6)	60 (414)
18 (64.4)	63 (434)
19 (66.2)	65 (448)
20 (68.0)	67 (462)
21 (69.8)	69 (476)
22 (71.6)	72 (496)
23 (73.4)	74 (510)
24 (75.2)	77 (531)
25 (77.0)	80 (552)
26 (78.8)	83 (572)
27 (80.6)	85 (586)
28 (82.4)	88 (607)
29 (84.2)	91 (627)
30 (86.0)	93 (641)
32 (89.6)	99 (683)
34 (93.2)	105 (724)
36 (96.8)	111 (765)
38 (100.4)	120 (827)
40 (104.0)	125 (862)

Temperature/pressure relationship data for R134a refrigerant

Temperature °C (°F)	Pressure psi (kPa)
−20 (−4.0)	4.5 (31)
−18 (−0.4)	6.3 (43)
−16 (3.2)	8.1 (56)
−14 (6.8)	10 (69)
−12 (10.4)	12 (83)
−10 (14.0)	14 (97)
−8 (17.6)	17 (117)
−6 (21.2)	19 (131)
−4 (24.8)	22 (152)
−2 (28.4)	25 (172)
0 (32.0)	28 (193)
1 (33.8)	29 (200)
2 (35.6)	31 (214)
3 (37.4)	32 (221)
4 (39.2)	34 (234)
5 (41.0)	36 (248)
6 (42.8)	38 (262)
7 (44.6)	40 (276)
8 (46.4)	41 (283)
9 (48.2)	43 (296)
10 (50.0)	45 (310)
11 (51.8)	47 (324)
12 (53.6)	49 (338)
13 (55.4)	52 (359)
14 (57.2)	54 (372)
15 (59.0)	56 (386)
16 (60.8)	58 (400)
17 (62.6)	61 (421)
18 (64.4)	63 (434)
19 (66.2)	65 (448)
20 (68.0)	68 (469)
21 (69.8)	71 (490)
22 (71.6)	73 (503)
23 (73.4)	76 (524)
24 (75.2)	79 (545)
25 (77.0)	82 (565)
26 (78.8)	84 (579)
27 (80.6)	87 (600)
28 (82.4)	90 (621)
29 (84.2)	93 (641)
30 (86.0)	97 (669)
32 (89.6)	103 (710)
34 (93.2)	110 (758)
36 (96.8)	117 (807)
38 (100.4)	124 (855)
40 (104.0)	132 (910)

Vehicle manufacturers' refrigerant and compressor oil recommendations

The Specifications given in the following chart are an example of those specified by a vehicle manufacturer. A full set of specifications is given in the professional edition of this book (ISBN 1 85960 556 7).

Alfa Romeo

Vehicle Model	Refrigerant type	Refrigerant quantity	Compressor oil type	Compressor oil quantity
33 (all petrol engine models)	R12	1150 grams	Suniso 5GS	–
33 (all diesel engine models)	R12	900 grams	Suniso 46	–
75 (all models)	R12	900 grams	Suniso 5GS	–
145 and 146 (all models up to 1998 except 1.6 and 2.0 Twin Spark)	R134a	700 grams	SP 10 PAG	240 ± 15 cc
145 and 146 (1.6 and 2.0 Twin Spark models up to 1998)	R134a	700 grams	SP10 PAG	150 ± 20 cc
155 (early petrol engine models)	R12 (check label on car)	–	Suniso 5GS	135 cc
155 (later petrol engine models up to 1998)	R134a (check label on car)	–	Sanden E13 M6	135 cc
155 (diesel engine models up to 1998)	R134a	–	Dens Oil 9 PAG	160 ± 20 cc
164 (early models)	R12 (check label on car)	1250 grams	Suniso 5GS	–
164 (later models up to 1998)	R134a (check label on car)	1200 grams	Sanden E13 M6 PAG	135 ± 15 cc
Spider 2.0 (up to 1993)	R12	–	Suniso 5GS	–
Spider 2.0 (from 1996 to 1998)	R134a	700 ± 50 grams	Dens Oil 9 PAG	290 ± 30 cc
GTV 2.0 (from 1996 to 1998)	R134a	700 ± 50 grams	Dens Oil 9 PAG	290 ± 30 cc
Spider V6 (from 1996 to 1998)	R134a	700 ± 50 grams	SP10 PAG	240 ± 15 cc

8

Compressor manufacturers' compressor PAG oil grade recommendations

The specifications given in the following chart are those specified by the compressor manufacturers for use in R134a systems.

Compressor manufacturer	Compressor type	PAG oil specification
Calsonic	–	ISO 50
Diesel Kiki (Sellec)	All rotary vane-type compressors	ISO 150
Diesel Kiki (Sellec)	All piston-type compressors	ISO 50
Ford	FX-15	ISO 100
Hala (Hyundai)	–	ISO 50
Harrison	All types	ISO 150
HCC	–	ISO 100
Nippondenso	All types	ISO 150
Sanden	SD7H5	ISO 150
Sanden	SD7V and TRS (scroll)	ISO 50
York (CCI)	Upright, 2 piston	ISO 50
Tama Scisakusyo	–	ISO 50
Zexel SC	Rotary DKV	ISO 150
Zexel	Wobbleplate DKW	ISO 50
Nissan	Swashplate	ISO 50
Nissan	Rotary	ISO 50
Seiko Seiki	–	ISO 150

Compressor manufacturers' compressor oil capacity recommendations

Compressor mineral oil capacities for R12 systems

The specifications given in the following chart are those specified by the compressor manufacturers for a complete system which has been discharged and flushed.

Compressor type	Mineral oil capacity
Harrison/Frigidaire	
A6	284 to 313 cc
R4	156 to 185 cc
DA 6 (Delco Air) and HR6	227 cc
V5	227 cc
Nippondenso	
Chrysler models	256 to 284 cc
Ford models up to 1981	369 cc
Ford models from 1982 to 1990 (except FX15 compressor)	227 to 284 cc
Ford FX-15 from 1982 to 1990	199 cc
6C17	256 cc
10PA17, 10PA20 and 10P15	227 cc
Sankyo/Sanden	
Cylinder-type compressors	199 to 227 cc
Scroll-type compressors	227 to 256 cc
Tecumseh	
4-cylinder compressors	227 cc
York	
Rotary vane compressors	170 to 227 cc

Compressor PAG oil capacities for R134a systems

The specifications given in the following chart are those specified by the compressor manufacturers for a complete system which has been discharged and flushed.

Compressor type	PAG oil capacity
Harrison/Frigidaire	
A6	313 cc
R4	170 cc
DA 6 (Delco Air), HR6 and HR6HE	227 cc
V5	227 cc
Nippondenso	
Chrysler C171, A590 and 6C17	256 cc
Chrysler 6E171	369 cc
Chrysler 10PA17	227 cc
Ford FS6 and 6P148	284 cc
Ford FX15	199 cc
Ford 10P15C, 10P15F and 10PA17C	227 cc
GM 10PA20 and 10P15	227 cc
Sankyo/Sanden	
SD508	170 cc
SD510 and 709	142 cc
SD510HD	199 cc
TR105 (scroll-type)	199 cc
Seiko/Seiki	
SS-170PSS, SS-805T and SS-806T	142 cc
SS-110P, SS-140P, SS-140PSS and SS-170P	170 cc
SS-110PSV, SS-140PSV, SS-146A, SS-170PSV, SS-811PB and SS-811PS2	199 cc
SS-200A	256 cc
Tecumseh	
HR980 and HG1000	313 cc
York	
206, 209 and 210	313 cc
Zexel/Diesel KIKI	
CD17 and DCW17	142 cc

Length (distance)

Inches (in)	x 25.4	= Millimetres (mm)	x 0.0394	= Inches (in)	
Feet (ft)	x 0.305	= Metres (m)	x 3.281	= Feet (ft)	
Miles	x 1.609	= Kilometres (km)	x 0.621	= Miles	

Volume (capacity)

Cubic inches (cu in; in³)	x 16.387	= Cubic centimetres (cc; cm³)	x 0.061	= Cubic inches (cu in; in³)	
Imperial pints (Imp pt)	x 0.568	= Litres (l)	x 1.76	= Imperial pints (Imp pt)	
Imperial quarts (Imp qt)	x 1.137	= Litres (l)	x 0.88	= Imperial quarts (Imp qt)	
Imperial quarts (Imp qt)	x 1.201	= US quarts (US qt)	x 0.833	= Imperial quarts (Imp qt)	
US quarts (US qt)	x 0.946	= Litres (l)	x 1.057	= US quarts (US qt)	
Imperial gallons (Imp gal)	x 4.546	= Litres (l)	x 0.22	= Imperial gallons (Imp gal)	
Imperial gallons (Imp gal)	x 1.201	= US gallons (US gal)	x 0.833	= Imperial gallons (Imp gal)	
US gallons (US gal)	x 3.785	= Litres (l)	x 0.264	= US gallons (US gal)	

Mass (weight)

Ounces (oz)	x 28.35	= Grams (g)	x 0.035	= Ounces (oz)	
Pounds (lb)	x 0.454	= Kilograms (kg)	x 2.205	= Pounds (lb)	

Force

Ounces-force (ozf; oz)	x 0.278	= Newtons (N)	x 3.6	= Ounces-force (ozf; oz)	
Pounds-force (lbf; lb)	x 4.448	= Newtons (N)	x 0.225	= Pounds-force (lbf; lb)	
Newtons (N)	x 0.1	= Kilograms-force (kgf; kg)	x 9.81	= Newtons (N)	

Pressure

Pounds-force per square inch (psi; lbf/in²; lb/in²)	x 0.070	= Kilograms-force per square centimetre (kgf/cm²; kg/cm²)	x 14.223	= Pounds-force per square inch (psi; lbf/in²; lb/in²)
Pounds-force per square inch (psi; lbf/in²; lb/in²)	x 0.068	= Atmospheres (atm)	x 14.696	= Pounds-force per square inch (psi; lbf/in²; lb/in²)
Pounds-force per square inch (psi; lbf/in²; lb/in²)	x 0.069	= Bars	x 14.5	= Pounds-force per square inch (psi; lbf/in²; lb/in²)
Pounds-force per square inch (psi; lbf/in²; lb/in²)	x 6.895	= Kilopascals (kPa)	x 0.145	= Pounds-force per square inch (psi; lbf/in²; lb/in²)
Kilopascals (kPa)	x 0.01	= Kilograms-force per square centimetre (kgf/cm²; kg/cm²)	x 98.1	= Kilopascals (kPa)
Millibar (mbar)	x 100	= Pascals (Pa)	x 0.01	= Millibar (mbar)
Millibar (mbar)	x 0.0145	= Pounds-force per square inch (psi; lbf/in²; lb/in²)	x 68.947	= Millibar (mbar)
Millibar (mbar)	x 0.75	= Millimetres of mercury (mmHg)	x 1.333	= Millibar (mbar)
Millibar (mbar)	x 0.401	= Inches of water (inH₂O)	x 2.491	= Millibar (mbar)
Millimetres of mercury (mmHg)	x 0.535	= Inches of water (inH₂O)	x 1.868	= Millimetres of mercury (mmHg)
Inches of water (inH₂O)	x 0.036	= Pounds-force per square inch (psi; lbf/in²; lb/in²)	x 27.68	= Inches of water (inH₂O)

Torque (moment of force)

Pounds-force inches (lbf in; lb in)	x 1.152	= Kilograms-force centimetre (kgf cm; kg cm)	x 0.868	= Pounds-force inches (lbf in; lb in)
Pounds-force inches (lbf in; lb in)	x 0.113	= Newton metres (Nm)	x 8.85	= Pounds-force inches (lbf in; lb in)
Pounds-force inches (lbf in; lb in)	x 0.083	= Pounds-force feet (lbf ft; lb ft)	x 12	= Pounds-force inches (lbf in; lb in)
Pounds-force feet (lbf ft; lb ft)	x 0.138	= Kilograms-force metres (kgf m; kg m)	x 7.233	= Pounds-force feet (lbf ft; lb ft)
Pounds-force feet (lbf ft; lb ft)	x 1.356	= Newton metres (Nm)	x 0.738	= Pounds-force feet (lbf ft; lb ft)
Newton metres (Nm)	x 0.102	= Kilograms-force metres (kgf m; kg m)	x 9.804	= Newton metres (Nm)

Power

Horsepower (hp)	x 745.7	= Watts (W)	x 0.0013	= Horsepower (hp)

Velocity (speed)

Miles per hour (miles/hr; mph)	x 1.609	= Kilometres per hour (km/hr; kph)	x 0.621	= Miles per hour (miles/hr; mph)

Fuel consumption*

Miles per gallon, Imperial (mpg)	x 0.354	= Kilometres per litre (km/l)	x 2.825	= Miles per gallon, Imperial (mpg)
Miles per gallon, US (mpg)	x 0.425	= Kilometres per litre (km/l)	x 2.352	= Miles per gallon, US (mpg)

Temperature

Degrees Fahrenheit = (°C x 1.8) + 32   Degrees Celsius (Degrees Centigrade; °C) = (°F - 32) x 0.56

It is common practice to convert from miles per gallon (mpg) to litres/100 kilometres (l/100km), where mpg x l/100 km = 282

Whenever servicing, repair or overhaul work is carried out on the car or its components, observe the following procedures and instructions. This will assist in carrying out the operation efficiently and to a professional standard of workmanship.

Joint mating faces and gaskets

When separating components at their mating faces, never insert screwdrivers or similar implements into the joint between the faces in order to prise them apart. This can cause severe damage which results in oil leaks, coolant leaks, etc upon reassembly. Separation is usually achieved by tapping along the joint with a soft-faced hammer in order to break the seal. However, note that this method may not be suitable where dowels are used for component location.

Where a gasket is used between the mating faces of two components, a new one must be fitted on reassembly; fit it dry unless otherwise stated in the repair procedure. Make sure that the mating faces are clean and dry, with all traces of old gasket removed. When cleaning a joint face, use a tool which is unlikely to score or damage the face, and remove any burrs or nicks with an oilstone or fine file.

Make sure that tapped holes are cleaned with a pipe cleaner, and keep them free of jointing compound, if this is being used, unless specifically instructed otherwise.

Ensure that all orifices, channels or pipes are clear, and blow through them, preferably using compressed air.

Oil seals

Oil seals can be removed by levering them out with a wide flat-bladed screwdriver or similar implement. Alternatively, a number of self-tapping screws may be screwed into the seal, and these used as a purchase for pliers or some similar device in order to pull the seal free.

Whenever an oil seal is removed from its working location, either individually or as part of an assembly, it should be renewed.

The very fine sealing lip of the seal is easily damaged, and will not seal if the surface it contacts is not completely clean and free from scratches, nicks or grooves. If the original sealing surface of the component cannot be restored, and the manufacturer has not made provision for slight relocation of the seal relative to the sealing surface, the component should be renewed.

Protect the lips of the seal from any surface which may damage them in the course of fitting. Use tape or a conical sleeve where possible. Lubricate the seal lips with oil before fitting and, on dual-lipped seals, fill the space between the lips with grease.

Unless otherwise stated, oil seals must be fitted with their sealing lips toward the lubricant to be sealed.

Use a tubular drift or block of wood of the appropriate size to install the seal and, if the seal housing is shouldered, drive the seal down to the shoulder. If the seal housing is unshouldered, the seal should be fitted with its face flush with the housing top face (unless otherwise instructed).

Screw threads and fastenings

Seized nuts, bolts and screws are quite a common occurrence where corrosion has set in, and the use of penetrating oil or releasing fluid will often overcome this problem if the offending item is soaked for a while before attempting to release it. The use of an impact driver may also provide a means of releasing such stubborn fastening devices, when used in conjunction with the appropriate screwdriver bit or socket. If none of these methods works, it may be necessary to resort to the careful application of heat, or the use of a hacksaw or nut splitter device.

Studs are usually removed by locking two nuts together on the threaded part, and then using a spanner on the lower nut to unscrew the stud. Studs or bolts which have broken off below the surface of the component in which they are mounted can sometimes be removed using a stud extractor. Always ensure that a blind tapped hole is completely free from oil, grease, water or other fluid before installing the bolt or stud. Failure to do this could cause the housing to crack due to the hydraulic action of the bolt or stud as it is screwed in.

When tightening a castellated nut to accept a split pin, tighten the nut to the specified torque, where applicable, and then tighten further to the next split pin hole. Never slacken the nut to align the split pin hole, unless stated in the repair procedure.

When checking or retightening a nut or bolt to a specified torque setting, slacken the nut or bolt by a quarter of a turn, and then retighten to the specified setting. However, this should not be attempted where angular tightening has been used.

For some screw fastenings, notably cylinder head bolts or nuts, torque wrench settings are no longer specified for the latter stages of tightening, "angle-tightening" being called up instead. Typically, a fairly low torque wrench setting will be applied to the bolts/nuts in the correct sequence, followed by one or more stages of tightening through specified angles.

Locknuts, locktabs and washers

Any fastening which will rotate against a component or housing during tightening should always have a washer between it and the relevant component or housing.

Spring or split washers should always be renewed when they are used to lock a critical component such as a big-end bearing retaining bolt or nut. Locktabs which are folded over to retain a nut or bolt should always be renewed.

Self-locking nuts can be re-used in non-critical areas, providing resistance can be felt when the locking portion passes over the bolt or stud thread. However, it should be noted that self-locking stiffnuts tend to lose their effectiveness after long periods of use, and should then be renewed as a matter of course.

Split pins must always be replaced with new ones of the correct size for the hole.

When thread-locking compound is found on the threads of a fastener which is to be re-used, it should be cleaned off with a wire brush and solvent, and fresh compound applied on reassembly.

Special tools

Some repair procedures in this manual entail the use of special tools such as a press, two or three-legged pullers, spring compressors, etc. Wherever possible, suitable readily-available alternatives to the manufacturer's special tools are described, and are shown in use. In some instances, where no alternative is possible, it has been necessary to resort to the use of a manufacturer's tool, and this has been done for reasons of safety as well as the efficient completion of the repair operation. Unless you are highly-skilled and have a thorough understanding of the procedures described, never attempt to bypass the use of any special tool when the procedure described specifies its use. Not only is there a very great risk of personal injury, but expensive damage could be caused to the components involved.

Environmental considerations

When disposing of used engine oil, brake fluid, antifreeze, etc, give due consideration to any detrimental environmental effects. Do not, for instance, pour any of the above liquids down drains into the general sewage system, or onto the ground to soak away. Many local council refuse tips provide a facility for waste oil disposal, as do some garages. If none of these facilities are available, consult your local Environmental Health Department, or the National Rivers Authority, for further advice.

With the universal tightening-up of legislation regarding the emission of environmentally-harmful substances from motor vehicles, most vehicles have tamperproof devices fitted to the main adjustment points of the fuel system. These devices are primarily designed to prevent unqualified persons from adjusting the fuel/air mixture, with the chance of a consequent increase in toxic emissions. If such devices are found during servicing or overhaul, they should, wherever possible, be renewed or refitted in accordance with the manufacturer's requirements or current legislation.

OIL CARE
FOLLOW THE CODE
OIL BANK LINE
0800 66 33 66

Note: It is antisocial and illegal to dump oil down the drain. To find the location of your local oil recycling bank, call this number free.

A

ABS (Anti-lock brake system) A system, usually electronically controlled, that senses incipient wheel lockup during braking and relieves hydraulic pressure at wheels that are about to skid.

Air bag An inflatable bag hidden in the steering wheel (driver's side) or the dash or glovebox (passenger side). In a head-on collision, the bags inflate, preventing the driver and front passenger from being thrown forward into the steering wheel or windscreen.

Air cleaner A metal or plastic housing, containing a filter element, which removes dust and dirt from the air being drawn into the engine.

Air filter element The actual filter in an air cleaner system, usually manufactured from pleated paper and requiring renewal at regular intervals.

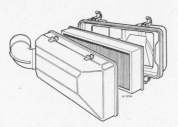

Air filter

Allen key A hexagonal wrench which fits into a recessed hexagonal hole.

Alligator clip A long-nosed spring-loaded metal clip with meshing teeth. Used to make temporary electrical connections.

Alternator A component in the electrical system which converts mechanical energy from a drivebelt into electrical energy to charge the battery and to operate the starting system, ignition system and electrical accessories.

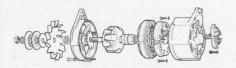

Alternator (exploded view)

Ampere (amp) A unit of measurement for the flow of electric current. One amp is the amount of current produced by one volt acting through a resistance of one ohm.

Anaerobic sealer A substance used to prevent bolts and screws from loosening. Anaerobic means that it does not require oxygen for activation. The Loctite brand is widely used.

Antifreeze A substance (usually ethylene glycol) mixed with water, and added to a vehicle's cooling system, to prevent freezing of the coolant in winter. Antifreeze also contains chemicals to inhibit corrosion and the formation of rust and other deposits that

would tend to clog the radiator and coolant passages and reduce cooling efficiency.

Anti-seize compound A coating that reduces the risk of seizing on fasteners that are subjected to high temperatures, such as exhaust manifold bolts and nuts.

Anti-seize compound

Asbestos A natural fibrous mineral with great heat resistance, commonly used in the composition of brake friction materials. Asbestos is a health hazard and the dust created by brake systems should never be inhaled or ingested.

Axle A shaft on which a wheel revolves, or which revolves with a wheel. Also, a solid beam that connects the two wheels at one end of the vehicle. An axle which also transmits power to the wheels is known as a live axle.

Axle assembly

Axleshaft A single rotating shaft, on either side of the differential, which delivers power from the final drive assembly to the drive wheels. Also called a driveshaft or a halfshaft.

B

Ball bearing An anti-friction bearing consisting of a hardened inner and outer race with hardened steel balls between two races.

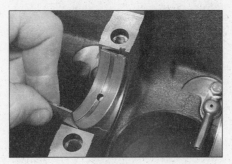

Bearing

Bearing The curved surface on a shaft or in a bore, or the part assembled into either, that permits relative motion between them with minimum wear and friction.

Big-end bearing The bearing in the end of the connecting rod that's attached to the crankshaft.

Bleed nipple A valve on a brake wheel cylinder, caliper or other hydraulic component that is opened to purge the hydraulic system of air. Also called a bleed screw.

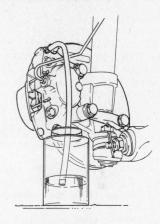

Brake bleeding

Brake bleeding Procedure for removing air from lines of a hydraulic brake system.

Brake disc The component of a disc brake that rotates with the wheels.

Brake drum The component of a drum brake that rotates with the wheels.

Brake linings The friction material which contacts the brake disc or drum to retard the vehicle's speed. The linings are bonded or riveted to the brake pads or shoes.

Brake pads The replaceable friction pads that pinch the brake disc when the brakes are applied. Brake pads consist of a friction material bonded or riveted to a rigid backing plate.

Brake shoe The crescent-shaped carrier to which the brake linings are mounted and which forces the lining against the rotating drum during braking.

Braking systems For more information on braking systems, consult the *Haynes Automotive Brake Manual*.

Breaker bar A long socket wrench handle providing greater leverage.

Bulkhead The insulated partition between the engine and the passenger compartment.

C

Caliper The non-rotating part of a disc-brake assembly that straddles the disc and carries the brake pads. The caliper also contains the hydraulic components that cause the pads to pinch the disc when the brakes are applied. A caliper is also a measuring tool that can be set to measure inside or outside dimensions of an object.

Glossary of technical terms

Camshaft A rotating shaft on which a series of cam lobes operate the valve mechanisms. The camshaft may be driven by gears, by sprockets and chain or by sprockets and a belt.

Canister A container in an evaporative emission control system; contains activated charcoal granules to trap vapours from the fuel system.

Canister

Carburettor A device which mixes fuel with air in the proper proportions to provide a desired power output from a spark ignition internal combustion engine.

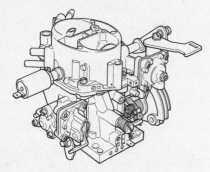
Carburettor

Castellated Resembling the parapets along the top of a castle wall. For example, a castellated balljoint stud nut.

Castellated nut

Castor In wheel alignment, the backward or forward tilt of the steering axis. Castor is positive when the steering axis is inclined rearward at the top.

Catalytic converter A silencer-like device in the exhaust system which converts certain pollutants in the exhaust gases into less harmful substances.

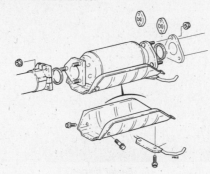
Catalytic converter

Circlip A ring-shaped clip used to prevent endwise movement of cylindrical parts and shafts. An internal circlip is installed in a groove in a housing; an external circlip fits into a groove on the outside of a cylindrical piece such as a shaft.

Clearance The amount of space between two parts. For example, between a piston and a cylinder, between a bearing and a journal, etc.

Coil spring A spiral of elastic steel found in various sizes throughout a vehicle, for example as a springing medium in the suspension and in the valve train.

Compression Reduction in volume, and increase in pressure and temperature, of a gas, caused by squeezing it into a smaller space.

Compression ratio The relationship between cylinder volume when the piston is at top dead centre and cylinder volume when the piston is at bottom dead centre.

Constant velocity (CV) joint A type of universal joint that cancels out vibrations caused by driving power being transmitted through an angle.

Core plug A disc or cup-shaped metal device inserted in a hole in a casting through which core was removed when the casting was formed. Also known as a freeze plug or expansion plug.

Crankcase The lower part of the engine block in which the crankshaft rotates.

Crankshaft The main rotating member, or shaft, running the length of the crankcase, with offset "throws" to which the connecting rods are attached.

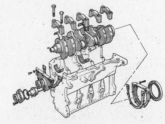
Crankshaft assembly

Crocodile clip See Alligator clip

D

Diagnostic code Code numbers obtained by accessing the diagnostic mode of an engine management computer. This code can be used to determine the area in the system where a malfunction may be located.

Disc brake A brake design incorporating a rotating disc onto which brake pads are squeezed. The resulting friction converts the energy of a moving vehicle into heat.

Double-overhead cam (DOHC) An engine that uses two overhead camshafts, usually one for the intake valves and one for the exhaust valves.

Drivebelt(s) The belt(s) used to drive accessories such as the alternator, water pump, power steering pump, air conditioning compressor, etc. off the crankshaft pulley.

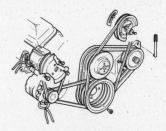
Accessory drivebelts

Driveshaft Any shaft used to transmit motion. Commonly used when referring to the axleshafts on a front wheel drive vehicle.

Driveshaft

Drum brake A type of brake using a drum-shaped metal cylinder attached to the inner surface of the wheel. When the brake pedal is pressed, curved brake shoes with friction linings press against the inside of the drum to slow or stop the vehicle.

Drum brake assembly

E

EGR valve A valve used to introduce exhaust gases into the intake air stream.

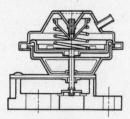

EGR valve

Electronic control unit (ECU) A computer which controls (for instance) ignition and fuel injection systems, or an anti-lock braking system. For more information refer to the *Haynes Automotive Electrical and Electronic Systems Manual*.

Electronic Fuel Injection (EFI) A computer controlled fuel system that distributes fuel through an injector located in each intake port of the engine.

Emergency brake A braking system, independent of the main hydraulic system, that can be used to slow or stop the vehicle if the primary brakes fail, or to hold the vehicle stationary even though the brake pedal isn't depressed. It usually consists of a hand lever that actuates either front or rear brakes mechanically through a series of cables and linkages. Also known as a handbrake or parking brake.

Endfloat The amount of lengthwise movement between two parts. As applied to a crankshaft, the distance that the crankshaft can move forward and back in the cylinder block.

Engine management system (EMS) A computer controlled system which manages the fuel injection and the ignition systems in an integrated fashion.

Exhaust manifold A part with several passages through which exhaust gases leave the engine combustion chambers and enter the exhaust pipe.

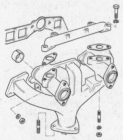

Exhaust manifold

F

Fan clutch A viscous (fluid) drive coupling device which permits variable engine fan speeds in relation to engine speeds.

Feeler blade A thin strip or blade of hardened steel, ground to an exact thickness, used to check or measure clearances between parts.

Feeler blade

Firing order The order in which the engine cylinders fire, or deliver their power strokes, beginning with the number one cylinder.

Flywheel A heavy spinning wheel in which energy is absorbed and stored by means of momentum. On cars, the flywheel is attached to the crankshaft to smooth out firing impulses.

Free play The amount of travel before any action takes place. The "looseness" in a linkage, or an assembly of parts, between the initial application of force and actual movement. For example, the distance the brake pedal moves before the pistons in the master cylinder are actuated.

Fuse An electrical device which protects a circuit against accidental overload. The typical fuse contains a soft piece of metal which is calibrated to melt at a predetermined current flow (expressed as amps) and break the circuit.

Fusible link A circuit protection device consisting of a conductor surrounded by heat-resistant insulation. The conductor is smaller than the wire it protects, so it acts as the weakest link in the circuit. Unlike a blown fuse, a failed fusible link must frequently be cut from the wire for replacement.

G

Gap The distance the spark must travel in jumping from the centre electrode to the side

Adjusting spark plug gap

electrode in a spark plug. Also refers to the spacing between the points in a contact breaker assembly in a conventional points-type ignition, or to the distance between the reluctor or rotor and the pickup coil in an electronic ignition.

Gasket Any thin, soft material - usually cork, cardboard, asbestos or soft metal - installed between two metal surfaces to ensure a good seal. For instance, the cylinder head gasket seals the joint between the block and the cylinder head.

Gasket

Gauge An instrument panel display used to monitor engine conditions. A gauge with a movable pointer on a dial or a fixed scale is an analogue gauge. A gauge with a numerical readout is called a digital gauge.

H

Halfshaft A rotating shaft that transmits power from the final drive unit to a drive wheel, usually when referring to a live rear axle.

Harmonic balancer A device designed to reduce torsion or twisting vibration in the crankshaft. May be incorporated in the crankshaft pulley. Also known as a vibration damper.

Hone An abrasive tool for correcting small irregularities or differences in diameter in an engine cylinder, brake cylinder, etc.

Hydraulic tappet A tappet that utilises hydraulic pressure from the engine's lubrication system to maintain zero clearance (constant contact with both camshaft and valve stem). Automatically adjusts to variation in valve stem length. Hydraulic tappets also reduce valve noise.

I

Ignition timing The moment at which the spark plug fires, usually expressed in the number of crankshaft degrees before the piston reaches the top of its stroke.

Inlet manifold A tube or housing with passages through which flows the air-fuel mixture (carburettor vehicles and vehicles with throttle body injection) or air only (port fuel-injected vehicles) to the port openings in the cylinder head.

J

Jump start Starting the engine of a vehicle with a discharged or weak battery by attaching jump leads from the weak battery to a charged or helper battery.

L

Load Sensing Proportioning Valve (LSPV) A brake hydraulic system control valve that works like a proportioning valve, but also takes into consideration the amount of weight carried by the rear axle.

Locknut A nut used to lock an adjustment nut, or other threaded component, in place. For example, a locknut is employed to keep the adjusting nut on the rocker arm in position.

Lockwasher A form of washer designed to prevent an attaching nut from working loose.

M

MacPherson strut A type of front suspension system devised by Earle MacPherson at Ford of England. In its original form, a simple lateral link with the anti-roll bar creates the lower control arm. A long strut - an integral coil spring and shock absorber - is mounted between the body and the steering knuckle. Many modern so-called MacPherson strut systems use a conventional lower A-arm and don't rely on the anti-roll bar for location.

Multimeter An electrical test instrument with the capability to measure voltage, current and resistance.

N

NOx Oxides of Nitrogen. A common toxic pollutant emitted by petrol and diesel engines at higher temperatures.

O

Ohm The unit of electrical resistance. One volt applied to a resistance of one ohm will produce a current of one amp.

Ohmmeter An instrument for measuring electrical resistance.

O-ring A type of sealing ring made of a special rubber-like material; in use, the O-ring is compressed into a groove to provide the sealing action.

O-ring

Overhead cam (ohc) engine An engine with the camshaft(s) located on top of the cylinder head(s).

Overhead valve (ohv) engine An engine with the valves located in the cylinder head, but with the camshaft located in the engine block.

Oxygen sensor A device installed in the engine exhaust manifold, which senses the oxygen content in the exhaust and converts this information into an electric current. Also called a Lambda sensor.

P

Phillips screw A type of screw head having a cross instead of a slot for a corresponding type of screwdriver.

Plastigage A thin strip of plastic thread, available in different sizes, used for measuring clearances. For example, a strip of Plastigage is laid across a bearing journal. The parts are assembled and dismantled; the width of the crushed strip indicates the clearance between journal and bearing.

Plastigage

Propeller shaft The long hollow tube with universal joints at both ends that carries power from the transmission to the differential on front-engined rear wheel drive vehicles.

Proportioning valve A hydraulic control valve which limits the amount of pressure to the rear brakes during panic stops to prevent wheel lock-up.

R

Rack-and-pinion steering A steering system with a pinion gear on the end of the steering shaft that mates with a rack (think of a geared wheel opened up and laid flat). When the steering wheel is turned, the pinion turns, moving the rack to the left or right. This movement is transmitted through the track rods to the steering arms at the wheels.

Radiator A liquid-to-air heat transfer device designed to reduce the temperature of the coolant in an internal combustion engine cooling system.

Refrigerant Any substance used as a heat transfer agent in an air-conditioning system. R-12 has been the principle refrigerant for many years; recently, however, manufacturers have begun using R-134a, a non-CFC substance that is considered less harmful to the ozone in the upper atmosphere.

Rocker arm A lever arm that rocks on a shaft or pivots on a stud. In an overhead valve engine, the rocker arm converts the upward movement of the pushrod into a downward movement to open a valve.

Rotor In a distributor, the rotating device inside the cap that connects the centre electrode and the outer terminals as it turns, distributing the high voltage from the coil secondary winding to the proper spark plug. Also, that part of an alternator which rotates inside the stator. Also, the rotating assembly of a turbocharger, including the compressor wheel, shaft and turbine wheel.

Runout The amount of wobble (in-and-out movement) of a gear or wheel as it's rotated. The amount a shaft rotates "out-of-true." The out-of-round condition of a rotating part.

S

Sealant A liquid or paste used to prevent leakage at a joint. Sometimes used in conjunction with a gasket.

Sealed beam lamp An older headlight design which integrates the reflector, lens and filaments into a hermetically-sealed one-piece unit. When a filament burns out or the lens cracks, the entire unit is simply replaced.

Serpentine drivebelt A single, long, wide accessory drivebelt that's used on some newer vehicles to drive all the accessories, instead of a series of smaller, shorter belts. Serpentine drivebelts are usually tensioned by an automatic tensioner.

Serpentine drivebelt

Shim Thin spacer, commonly used to adjust the clearance or relative positions between two parts. For example, shims inserted into or under bucket tappets control valve clearances. Clearance is adjusted by changing the thickness of the shim.

Slide hammer A special puller that screws into or hooks onto a component such as a shaft or bearing; a heavy sliding handle on the shaft bottoms against the end of the shaft to knock the component free.

Sprocket A tooth or projection on the periphery of a wheel, shaped to engage with a chain or drivebelt. Commonly used to refer to the sprocket wheel itself.

Starter inhibitor switch On vehicles with an automatic transmission, a switch that prevents starting if the vehicle is not in Neutral or Park.

Strut See MacPherson strut.

T

Tappet A cylindrical component which transmits motion from the cam to the valve stem, either directly or via a pushrod and rocker arm. Also called a cam follower.

Thermostat A heat-controlled valve that regulates the flow of coolant between the cylinder block and the radiator, so maintaining optimum engine operating temperature. A thermostat is also used in some air cleaners in which the temperature is regulated.

Thrust bearing The bearing in the clutch assembly that is moved in to the release levers by clutch pedal action to disengage the clutch. Also referred to as a release bearing.

Timing belt A toothed belt which drives the camshaft. Serious engine damage may result if it breaks in service.

Timing chain A chain which drives the camshaft.

Toe-in The amount the front wheels are closer together at the front than at the rear. On rear wheel drive vehicles, a slight amount of toe-in is usually specified to keep the front wheels running parallel on the road by offsetting other forces that tend to spread the wheels apart.

Toe-out The amount the front wheels are closer together at the rear than at the front. On front wheel drive vehicles, a slight amount of toe-out is usually specified.

Tools For full information on choosing and using tools, refer to the *Haynes Automotive Tools Manual.*

Tracer A stripe of a second colour applied to a wire insulator to distinguish that wire from another one with the same colour insulator.

Tune-up A process of accurate and careful adjustments and parts replacement to obtain the best possible engine performance.

Turbocharger A centrifugal device, driven by exhaust gases, that pressurises the intake air. Normally used to increase the power output from a given engine displacement, but can also be used primarily to reduce exhaust emissions (as on VW's "Umwelt" Diesel engine).

U

Universal joint or U-joint A double-pivoted connection for transmitting power from a driving to a driven shaft through an angle. A U-joint consists of two Y-shaped yokes and a cross-shaped member called the spider.

V

Valve A device through which the flow of liquid, gas, vacuum, or loose material in bulk may be started, stopped, or regulated by a movable part that opens, shuts, or partially obstructs one or more ports or passageways. A valve is also the movable part of such a device.

Valve clearance The clearance between the valve tip (the end of the valve stem) and the rocker arm or tappet. The valve clearance is measured when the valve is closed.

Vernier caliper A precision measuring instrument that measures inside and outside dimensions. Not quite as accurate as a micrometer, but more convenient.

Viscosity The thickness of a liquid or its resistance to flow.

Volt A unit for expressing electrical "pressure" in a circuit. One volt that will produce a current of one ampere through a resistance of one ohm.

W

Welding Various processes used to join metal items by heating the areas to be joined to a molten state and fusing them together. For more information refer to the *Haynes Automotive Welding Manual.*

Wiring diagram A drawing portraying the components and wires in a vehicle's electrical system, using standardised symbols. For more information refer to the *Haynes Automotive Electrical and Electronic Systems Manual.*

Introduction

A selection of good tools is a fundamental requirement for anyone contemplating the maintenance and repair of a motor vehicle. For the owner who does not possess any, their purchase will prove a considerable expense, offsetting some of the savings made by doing-it-yourself. However, provided that the tools purchased meet the relevant national safety standards and are of good quality, they will last for many years and prove an extremely worthwhile investment.

To help the average owner to decide which tools are needed to carry out the various tasks detailed in this manual, we have compiled three lists of tools under the following headings: *Maintenance and minor repair, Repair and overhaul*, and *Special*. Newcomers to practical mechanics should start off with the *Maintenance and minor repair* tool kit, and confine themselves to the simpler jobs around the vehicle. Then, as confidence and experience grow, more difficult tasks can be undertaken, with extra tools being purchased as, and when, they are needed. In this way, a *Maintenance and minor repair* tool kit can be built up into a *Repair and overhaul* tool kit over a considerable period of time, without any major cash outlays. The experienced do-it-yourselfer will have a tool kit good enough for most repair and overhaul procedures, and will add tools from the *Special* category when it is felt that the expense is justified by the amount of use to which these tools will be put.

Maintenance and minor repair tool kit

The tools given in this list should be considered as a minimum requirement if routine maintenance, servicing and minor repair operations are to be undertaken. We recommend the purchase of combination spanners (ring one end, open-ended the other); although more expensive than open-ended ones, they do give the advantages of both types of spanner.

☐ *Combination spanners:*
  Metric - 8 to 19 mm inclusive
☐ *Adjustable spanner - 35 mm jaw (approx.)*
☐ *Spark plug spanner (with rubber insert) - petrol models*
☐ *Spark plug gap adjustment tool - petrol models*
☐ *Set of feeler gauges*
☐ *Brake bleed nipple spanner*
☐ *Screwdrivers:*
  Flat blade - 100 mm long x 6 mm dia
  Cross blade - 100 mm long x 6 mm dia
  Torx - various sizes (not all vehicles)
☐ *Combination pliers*
☐ *Hacksaw (junior)*
☐ *Tyre pump*
☐ *Tyre pressure gauge*
☐ *Oil can*
☐ *Oil filter removal tool*
☐ *Fine emery cloth*
☐ *Wire brush (small)*
☐ *Funnel (medium size)*
☐ *Sump drain plug key (not all vehicles)*

Repair and overhaul tool kit

These tools are virtually essential for anyone undertaking any major repairs to a motor vehicle, and are additional to those given in the *Maintenance and minor repair* list. Included in this list is a comprehensive set of sockets. Although these are expensive, they will be found invaluable as they are so versatile - particularly if various drives are included in the set. We recommend the half-inch square-drive type, as this can be used with most proprietary torque wrenches.

The tools in this list will sometimes need to be supplemented by tools from the *Special* list:

☐ *Sockets (or box spanners) to cover range in previous list (including Torx sockets)*
☐ *Reversible ratchet drive (for use with sockets)*
☐ *Extension piece, 250 mm (for use with sockets)*
☐ *Universal joint (for use with sockets)*
☐ *Flexible handle or sliding T "breaker bar" (for use with sockets)*
☐ *Torque wrench (for use with sockets)*
☐ *Self-locking grips*
☐ *Ball pein hammer*
☐ *Soft-faced mallet (plastic or rubber)*
☐ *Screwdrivers:*
  Flat blade - long & sturdy, short (chubby), and narrow (electrician's) types
  Cross blade - long & sturdy, and short (chubby) types
☐ *Pliers:*
  Long-nosed
  Side cutters (electrician's)
  Circlip (internal and external)
☐ *Cold chisel - 25 mm*
☐ *Scriber*
☐ *Scraper*
☐ *Centre-punch*
☐ *Pin punch*
☐ *Hacksaw*
☐ *Brake hose clamp*
☐ *Brake/clutch bleeding kit*
☐ *Selection of twist drills*
☐ *Steel rule/straight-edge*
☐ *Allen keys (inc. splined/Torx type)*
☐ *Selection of files*
☐ *Wire brush*
☐ *Axle stands*
☐ *Jack (strong trolley or hydraulic type)*
☐ *Light with extension lead*
☐ *Universal electrical multi-meter*

Sockets and reversible ratchet drive

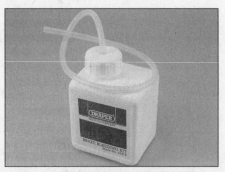

Brake bleeding kit

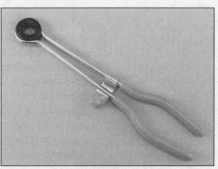

Hose clamp

Torx key, socket and bit

Angular-tightening gauge

Special tools

The tools in this list are those which are not used regularly, are expensive to buy, or which need to be used in accordance with their manufacturers' instructions. Unless relatively difficult mechanical jobs are undertaken frequently, it will not be economic to buy many of these tools. Where this is the case, you could consider clubbing together with friends (or joining a motorists' club) to make a joint purchase, or borrowing the tools against a deposit from a local garage or tool hire specialist. It is worth noting that many of the larger DIY superstores now carry a large range of special tools for hire at modest rates.

The following list contains only those tools and instruments freely available to the public, and not those special tools produced by the vehicle manufacturer specifically for its dealer network. You will find occasional references to these manufacturers' special tools in the text of this manual. Generally, an alternative method of doing the job without the vehicle manufacturers' special tool is given. However, sometimes there is no alternative to using them. Where this is the case and the relevant tool cannot be bought or borrowed, you will have to entrust the work to a dealer.

☐ *Angular-tightening gauge*
☐ *Valve spring compressor*
☐ *Valve grinding tool*
☐ *Piston ring compressor*
☐ *Piston ring removal/installation tool*
☐ *Cylinder bore hone*
☐ *Balljoint separator*
☐ *Coil spring compressors (where applicable)*
☐ *Two/three-legged hub and bearing puller*
☐ *Impact screwdriver*
☐ *Micrometer and/or vernier calipers*
☐ *Dial gauge*
☐ *Stroboscopic timing light*
☐ *Dwell angle meter/tachometer*
☐ *Fault code reader*
☐ *Cylinder compression gauge*
☐ *Hand-operated vacuum pump and gauge*
☐ *Clutch plate alignment set*
☐ *Brake shoe steady spring cup removal tool*
☐ *Bush and bearing removal/installation set*
☐ *Stud extractors*
☐ *Tap and die set*
☐ *Lifting tackle*
☐ *Trolley jack*

Buying tools

Reputable motor accessory shops and superstores often offer excellent quality tools at discount prices, so it pays to shop around.

Remember, you don't have to buy the most expensive items on the shelf, but it is always advisable to steer clear of the very cheap tools. Beware of 'bargains' offered on market stalls or at car boot sales. There are plenty of good tools around at reasonable prices, but always aim to purchase items which meet the relevant national safety standards. If in doubt, ask the proprietor or manager of the shop for advice before making a purchase.

Care and maintenance of tools

Having purchased a reasonable tool kit, it is necessary to keep the tools in a clean and serviceable condition. After use, always wipe off any dirt, grease and metal particles using a clean, dry cloth, before putting the tools away. Never leave them lying around after they have been used. A simple tool rack on the garage or workshop wall for items such as screwdrivers and pliers is a good idea. Store all normal spanners and sockets in a metal box. Any measuring instruments, gauges, meters, etc, must be carefully stored where they cannot be damaged or become rusty.

Take a little care when tools are used. Hammer heads inevitably become marked, and screwdrivers lose the keen edge on their blades from time to time. A little timely attention with emery cloth or a file will soon restore items like this to a good finish.

Working facilities

Not to be forgotten when discussing tools is the workshop itself. If anything more than routine maintenance is to be carried out, a suitable working area becomes essential.

It is appreciated that many an owner-mechanic is forced by circumstances to remove an engine or similar item without the benefit of a garage or workshop. Having done this, any repairs should always be done under the cover of a roof.

Wherever possible, any dismantling should be done on a clean, flat workbench or table at a suitable working height.

Any workbench needs a vice; one with a jaw opening of 100 mm is suitable for most jobs. As mentioned previously, some clean dry storage space is also required for tools, as well as for any lubricants, cleaning fluids, touch-up paints etc, which become necessary.

Another item which may be required, and which has a much more general usage, is an electric drill with a chuck capacity of at least 8 mm. This, together with a good range of twist drills, is virtually essential for fitting accessories.

Last, but not least, always keep a supply of old newspapers and clean, lint-free rags available, and try to keep any working area as clean as possible.

Micrometers

Dial test indicator ("dial gauge")

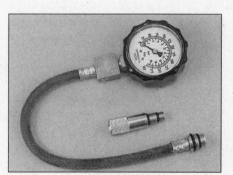
Strap wrench

Compression tester

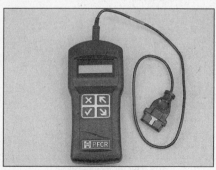
Fault code reader

A

Accumulator - 2•15, 6•33
Acknowledgements - 0•4
Adapter fittings for manifold gauges - 4•5
Air bags - 5•2
Air conditioning system components - 2•1 *et seq*
    air conditioning system types - 2•2, 2•3
    accumulator - 2•15
    ambient temperature switch - 2•22
    anti-dieseling relay - 2•30
    blower fan and motor - 2•13
    closed throttle switch - 2•29
    compressor - 2•4, 2•7, 2•9, 2•19, 2•25, 2•30, 2•33
    condenser - 2•12, 2•13, 2•26
    constant run relay - 2•30
    coolant high temperature switch - 2•30
    cooling system fan temperature switch - 2•26
    driveability controls - 2•29
    evaporator - 2•13, 2•26
    Evaporator Pressure Regulator (EPR) valve - 2•29
    Evaporator-Equalised Valves-In-Receiver (EEVIR) - 2•29
    expansion valve - 2•16, 2•17
    filter/drier - 2•14
    high pressure cut-out switch - 2•20
    high pressure fan switch - 2•26
    high pressure relief valve - 2•30
    low pressure cut-out switch - 2•20
    low vacuum switch - 2•29
    on switch - 2•26
    orifice tube - 2•18
    Pilot Operated Absolute Suction Throttling
        Valve (POA STV) - 2•27
    power brake switch - 2•30
    power steering pressure switch - 2•30
    pressure-sensitive (cycling) switch - 2•22
    pressure-sensitive fan switch - 2•26
    R12 - 2•32
    R134a - 2•32
    refrigerants - 2•31, 2•32
    Suction Throttling Valve (STV) - 2•26
    temperature sensing bulb and capillary tube - 2•17
    thermal fuse/superheat switch - 2•23
    thermostatic switch - 2•24
    time delay relay - 2•29
    trinary switch - 2•21, 2•26
    Valves-In-Receiver (VIR) - 2•28
    wide-open throttle switch - 2•29
Air conditioning system service specifications - 8•1 *et seq*
Ambient temperature switch - 2•22
Anti-dieseling relay - 2•30
Asbestos - 5•2

B

Basic theory of air conditioning system operation - 1•1 *et seq*
    air conditioning - 1•6, 1•7
    CFCs - 1•12
    comfort zone - 1•2
    conduction - 1•4, 1•5
    convection - 1•4
    global warming - 1•13
    greenhouse effect - 1•13
    heat - 1•3
    heat transfer - 1•4, 1•7
    latent heat of vaporisation - 1•8
    ozone layer - 1•11
    pressure - 1•8
    protecting the environment - 1•13
    radiation - 1•5
    refrigerants - 1•11, 1•12
Battery - 5•2
    voltage - 7•4
Blower fan and motor - 2•13
Bulk refrigerant cylinders - 4•7
Burning - 5•2

C

Capillary tube - 2•17
CFCs - 1•12
Charging a system - 6•25
    liquid charging - 6•26
    vapour charging - 6•25
Charging cylinder - 4•11
Climate control systems - 3•9, 7•12
Closed throttle switch - 2•29
Clothing - 5•3
Comfort zone - 1•2
Comparator - 4•8, 6•16
Compressor - 2•4, 6•34
    clutch - 2•11
    clutch coil - 7•12, 7•12
    delay timer - 2•30
    leaks - 6•31
    lubrication - 2•4
    oils - 2•33, 4•13, 6•17, 6•18, 6•19, 8•3, 8•4, 8•5
    oil injector - 4•13
    piston-type compressors - 2•4
    reed valve - 6•34
    rotary vane-type compressors - 2•8
    scroll-type compressors - 2•9
    variable-displacement piston-type compressors - 2•7

Compressor controls - 2•19
  ambient temperature switch - 2•22
  crankcase pressure control valve - 2•25
  high pressure cut-out switch - 2•20
  low pressure cut-out switch - 2•20
  pressure-sensitive (cycling) switch - 2•22
  thermal fuse/superheat switch - 2•23
  thermostatic switch - 2•24
  trinary switch - 2•21
Condenser - 2•12, 6•33
Condenser fan - 2•13, 6•8, 7•4
  controls - 2•26
Conduction - 1•4, 1•5
Constant run relay - 2•30
Contents - 0•2
Convection - 1•4
Cooling system
  fan temperature switch - 2•26
  high temperature switch - 2•30
Crankcase pressure control valve - 2•25
Cylinder heater - 4•13

D

Desiccant - 6•33
Diesel injection equipment - 5•2
Discharging a system - 6•20, 6•21
Driveability controls - 2•29
  anti-dieseling relay - 2•30
  closed throttle switch - 2•29
  compressor delay timer - 2•30
  constant run relay - 2•30
  engine coolant high temperature switch - 2•30
  high pressure relief valve - 2•30
  low vacuum switch - 2•29
  power brake switch - 2•30
  power steering pressure switch - 2•30
  time delay relay - 2•29
  wide-open throttle switch - 2•29

E

Electric shock - 5•2
Environment protection - 1•13
Evacuating a system - 6•23
Evaporator - 2•13, 6•33
Evaporator controls - 2•26
  Evaporator Pressure Regulator (EPR) system - 3•8
  Evaporator Pressure Regulator (EPR) valve - 2•29
  Evaporator-Equalised Valves-In-Receiver (EEVIR) - 2•29
  Pilot Operated Absolute Suction Throttling Valve
    (POA STV) - 2•27
  Suction Throttling Valve (STV) - 2•26
  Valves-In-Receiver (VIR) - 2•28
Evaporator-Equalised Valves-In-Receiver (EEVIR) - 2•29
Expansion valve - 2•16, 6•34
  operation - 2•17
  spring - 2•17
  system - 3•4
  temperature sensing bulb and capillary tube - 2•17

F

Fan
  high pressure switch - 2•26
  pressure-sensitive switch - 2•26
  temperature switch - 2•26
  trinary switch - 2•26
Fault diagnosis - 7•1 *et seq*
  battery voltage - 7•4
  climate control systems - 7•13
  compressor clutch coil - 7•12
  compressor clutch does not engage - 7•10
  condenser cooling fan - 7•4
  cool air output inadequate - 7•7
  flowcharts - 7•4
  ice - 7•11
  intermittent cooling airflow - 7•8
  manifold gauge tests - 7•14
  no cooling airflow - 7•5, 7•6
  noisy in operation - 7•9
  procedures - 7•4, 7•11
  sequence - 7•3
  sloshing noise around corners - 7•11
  smells - 7•11
  system appears to be working, but warm air is
    delivered - 7•11
  system operates when first switched on, then stops
    shortly afterwards - 7•12
  water under vehicle - 7•11
  windows inside vehicle mist up - 7•11
Filter/drier - 2•14, 6•33
Fire - 5•2
Flushing - 6•29
  equipment - 4•13
Fume or gas intoxication - 5•2

G

Gas analyser - 4•14, 6•17
Gaskets - 6•31
Global warming - 1•13
Greenhouse effect - 1•13

H

Halide torch - 4•10
Heat - 1•3
Heat transfer - 1•4, 1•7
    convection, conduction and radiation - 1•4
    heat moves from warmer to cooler substances - 1•4
High pressure
    cut-out switch - 2•20
    fan switch - 2•26
    relief valve - 2•30
Hoses - 4•4, 6•31, 6•32
Hydrofluoric acid - 5•2

I

Ice - 7•11
Introduction - 0•4

L

Latent heat of vaporisation - 1•8
Leak detection - 4•9, 6•13, 6•14, 6•28
    bubble solution - 4•9, 6•13
    by sight - 6•13
    electronic leak detection - 4•10, 6•15
    halide torch - 4•10
    tracer dye - 4•10, 6•14
Leaks - 6•31
    compressor seal leaks - 6•31
    deteriorated O-rings or gaskets - 6•31, 6•32
    loose fittings or connections - 6•31, 6•32
    porous, damaged or deteriorated hoses - 6•31, 6•32
Liquid charging - 6•26
Low pressure cut-out switch - 2•20
Low vacuum switch - 2•29

M

Manifold (test) gauge set - 4•3, 4•5, 6•10
    connecting a manifold gauge set - 4•5
    gauges - 4•3
    hoses - 4•4
    manifold hand valves - 4•4
    pressure measurement - 4•5
    service adapter fittings for manifold gauges - 4•5
    tests - 7•14, 7•15
    vacuum measurement - 4•5
Manually-controlled air conditioning systems - 3•4
Metal pipes - 6•32
Multimeter - 4•12

O

Oil level dipsticks - 4•12
Orifice tube - 2•18, 3•5, 6•34
    removal tool - 4•14
O-rings - 6•31, 6•32
Oxygen-Free Nitrogen (OFN) - 6•22
    pressure testing equipment - 4•13

P

Pilot Operated Absolute Suction Throttling Valve (POA STV) - 2•27
Piston-type compressors - 2•4
Poisonous or irritant substances - 5•2
Power brake switch - 2•30
Power steering pressure switch - 2•30
Pressure - 1•8, 6•12, 6•13
    high and low sides - 3•2, 3•3
    measurement - 4•5
    testing - 6•22, 6•22
Pressure-sensitive
    cycling switch - 2•22
    fan switch - 2•26

R

R12 - 2•32
R134a - 2•32
Radiation - 1•4, 1•5
Reclaiming refrigerant - 6•21
Recycling
    cylinders - 4•8
    machine - 4•13
    refrigerant - 6•21
Refrigerant - 1•11, 2•4, 2•31, 2•32
    charging cylinder - 4•11
    comparator - 4•8
    cylinder heater - 4•13
    cylinders - 4•7, 4•8
    line connections - 6•30
    recommendations - 8•3
    recovery machine - 4•7
    recycling machine - 4•13
    temperature/pressure relationships - 8•2
    CFCs - 1•12
    global warming - 1•13
    greenhouse effect - 1•13
    ozone layer - 1•11
    protecting the environment - 1•13
Repair procedures - 6•30
Rotary vane-type
    compressors - 2•8
    vacuum pump - 4•6

S

Safety - 5•1 *et seq*
    air bags - 5•2
    asbestos - 5•2
    battery - 5•2
    burning - 5•2
    clothing - 5•3
    crushing - 5•2
    diesel injection equipment - 5•2
    electric shock - 5•2
    equipment - 4•2
    fire - 5•2
    fume or gas intoxication - 5•2
    hazards - 5•3
    hydrofluoric acid - 5•2
    poisonous or irritant substances - 5•2
    precautions - 5•3
    scalding - 5•2
Scalding - 5•2
Scales - 4•12
Schrader valves - 6•4
Screw-fit connections - 6•30, 6•32
Scroll-type compressors - 2•9
Service and repair procedures - 6•1 *et seq*
    accumulator - 6•33
    annual system check - 6•7
    bubble solution - 6•13
    charging a system - 6•25
    comparator - 6•16
    compressor - 6•17, 6•18, 6•19, 6•34
    condenser - 6•8, 6•33
    desiccant - 6•33
    discharging a system - 6•20
    do's and don'ts - 6•2
    electronic leak detector - 6•15
    evacuating a system - 6•23
    evaporator - 6•33
    expansion valve - 6•34
    filter/drier - 6•33
    flushing - 6•29
    gas analyser - 6•17
    gaskets - 6•31
    hose fittings - 6•31, 6•32
    identifying the refrigerant - 6•15
    leak testing - 6•13, 6•28
    leaks - 6•31
    loose fittings or connections - 6•31, 6•32
    manifold (test) gauge set - 6•10
    metal pipes - 6•32
    orifice tube - 6•34
    O-rings - 6•31, 6•32
    Oxygen-Free Nitrogen (OFN) - 6•22
    preliminary work - 6•8
    pressure - 6•12, 6•13, 6•22
    reclaiming refrigerant - 6•21
    recycling refrigerant - 6•21
    refrigerant line connections - 6•30
    regular servicing - 6•7
    repair procedures - 6•30
    Schrader valves - 6•4
    screw-fit connections - 6•30, 6•32
    service procedures - 6•8
    service valves - 6•3, 6•6
    sight glass - 6•9
    spring-lock couplings - 6•30, 6•32
    stabilising the system - 6•11
    stem-type valves - 6•5
    temperature - 6•12, 6•13
    tracer dye - 6•14
    vapour charging - 6•25
    visual checks - 6•8
Service valves - 6•3, 6•6
    Schrader valves - 6•4
    stem-type valves - 6•5
Sight glass - 6•9
Sloshing noise around corners - 7•11
Smells - 7•11
Spring-lock couplings - 6•30, 6•32
    release tool kit - 4•14
Stem-type valves - 6•5
Suction Throttling Valve (STV) - 2•26, 3•6
Superheat switch - 2•23

T

Temperature - 6•12
Temperature sensing bulb and capillary tube - 2•17
Thermal fuse/superheat switch - 2•23
Thermometer - 4•9
Thermostatic switch - 2•24
Time delay relay - 2•29
Tools and equipment - 4•1 *et seq*
    bubble solution - 4•9
    bulk refrigerant cylinders - 4•7
    charging cylinder - 4•11
    comparator - 4•8
    component flushing equipment - 4•13
    compressor oil - 4•13
    cylinder heater - 4•13
    cylinders - 4•7, 4•8
    gas analyser - 4•14
    halide torch - 4•10

hoses - 4•4
leak detection equipment - 4•9
manifold (test) gauge set - 4•3, 4•5
manifold hand valves - 4•4
multimeter - 4•12
oil level dipsticks - 4•12
orifice tube removal tool - 4•14
Oxygen-Free Nitrogen (OFN) pressure testing
    equipment - 4•13
pressure gauge readings - 4•5
pressure measurement - 4•5
recycling cylinders - 4•7, 4•8
refrigerant reclaim (recycling) machine - 4•13
refrigerant recovery machine - 4•7
safety equipment - 4•2
scales - 4•12
service adapter fittings for manifold gauges - 4•5
spring-lock coupling release tool kit - 4•14
thermometer - 4•9
tracer dye - 4•10
vacuum measurement - 4•5
vacuum pump - 4•6
vacuum readings - 4•5
waste refrigerant (reclaim) cylinders - 4•8
Tracer dye - 4•10, 6•14
Trinary switch - 2•21, 2•26

Typical air conditioning systems - 3•1 *et seq*
automatic air conditioning/climate control systems - 3•9
Evaporator Pressure Regulator (EPR) system - 3•8
expansion valve system - 3•4
manually-controlled air conditioning systems - 3•4
orifice tube (or 'accumulator') system - 3•5
Suction Throttling Valve (STV) system - 3•6
Valves-In-Receiver (VIR) system - 3•7

V

Vacuum measurement - 4•5
Vacuum pump - 4•6, 6•23
Valves-In-Receiver (VIR) - 2•28, 3•7
Vapour charging - 6•25
Variable-displacement piston-type compressors - 2•7
Venturi-type vacuum pump - 4•6

W

Waste refrigerant (reclaim) cylinders - 4•8
Water under vehicle - 7•11
Wide-open throttle switch - 2•29
Windows inside vehicle mist up - 7•11

Haynes Manuals – The Complete List

Title	Book No.
ALFA ROMEO	
Alfa Romeo Alfasud/Sprint (74 - 88) up to F	0292
Alfa Romeo Alfetta (73 - 87) up to E	0531
ALFA ROMEO	
Audi 80 (72 - Feb 79) up to T	0207
Audi 80, 90 (79 - Oct 86) up to D & Coupe (81 - Nov 88) up to F	0605
Audi 80, 90 (Oct 86 - 90) D to H & Coupe (Nov 88 - 90) F to H	1491
Audi 100 (Oct 82 - 90) up to H & 200 (Feb 84 - Oct 89) A to G	0907
Audi 100 & A6 Petrol & Diesel (May 91 - May 97) H to P	3504
Audi A4 (95 - Feb 00) M to V	3575
AUSTIN	
Austin/MG/Rover Maestro 1.3 & 1.6 (83 - 95) up to M	0922
Austin/MG Metro (80 - May 90) up to G	0718
Austin/Rover Montego 1.3 & 1.6 (84 - 94) A to L	1066
Austin/MG/Rover Montego 2.0 (84 - 95) A to M	1067
Mini (59 - 69) up to H	0527
Mini (69 - Oct 96) up to P	0646
Austin/Rover 2.0 litre Diesel Engine (86 - 93) C to L	1857
BEDFORD	
Bedford CF (69 - 87) up to E	0163
Bedford/Vauxhall Rascal & Suzuki Supercarry (86 - Oct 94) C to M	3015
BMW	
BMW 316, 320 & 320i (4-cyl) (75 - Feb 83) up to Y	0276
BMW 320, 320i, 323i & 325i (6-cyl) (Oct 77 - Sept 87) up to E	0815
BMW 3-Series (Apr 91 - 96) H to N	3210
BMW 3- & 5-Series (sohc) (81 - 91) up to J	1948
BMW 520i & 525e (Oct 81 - June 88) up to E	1560
BMW 525, 528 & 528i (73 - Sept 81) up to X	0632
CITROEN	
Citroën 2CV, Ami & Dyane (67 - 90) up to H	0196
Citroën AX Petrol & Diesel (87 - 97) D to P	3014
Citroën BX (83 - 94) A to L	0908
Citroën C15 Van Petrol & Diesel (89 - Oct 98) F to S	3509
Citroën CX (75 - 88) up to F	0528
Citroën Saxo Petrol & Diesel (96 - 98) N to S	3506
Citroën Visa (79 - 88) up to F	0620
Citroën Xantia Petrol & Diesel (93 - 98) K to S	3082
Citroën XM Petrol & Diesel (89 - 98) G to R	3451
Citroën ZX Diesel (91 - 93) J to L	1922
Citroën ZX Petrol (91 - 94) H to M	1881
Citroën 1.7 & 1.9 litre Diesel Engine (84 - 96) A to N	1379
COLT	
Colt/Mitsubishi 1200, 1250 & 1400 (79 - May 84) up to A	0600
FIAT	
Fiat 500 (57 - 73) up to M	0090
Fiat Cinquecento (93 - 98) K to R	3501
Fiat Panda (81 - 95) up to M	0793
Fiat Punto Petrol & Diesel (94 - Oct 99) L to V	3251
Fiat Regata (84 - 88) A to F	1167
Fiat Tipo (88 - 91) E to J	1625
Fiat Uno (83 - 95) up to M	0923
Fiat X1/9 (74 - 89) up to G	0273
FORD	
Ford Capri II (& III) 1.6 & 2.0 (74 - 87) up to E	0283
Ford Capri II (& III) 2.8 & 3.0 (74 - 87) up to E	1309
Ford Cortina Mk IV (& V) 1.6 & 2.0 (76 - 83) up to A	0343
Ford Escort (75 - Aug 80) up to V	0280
Ford Escort (Sept 80 - Sept 90) up to H	0686
Ford Escort & Orion (Sept 90 - 97) H to P	1737
Ford Escort Mk II Mexico, RS 1600 & RS 2000 (75 - 80) up to W	0735
Ford Fiesta (76 - Aug 83) up to Y	0334
Ford Fiesta (Aug 83 - Feb 89) A to F	1030
Ford Fiesta (Feb 89 - Oct 95) F to N	1595
Ford Fiesta Petrol & Diesel (Oct 95 - 97) N to R	3397
Ford Granada (Sept 77 - Feb 85) up to B	0481
Ford Granada & Scorpio (Mar 85 - 94) B to M	1245
Ford Ka (96 - 99) P to T	3570
Ford Mondeo Petrol (93 - 99) K to T	1923
Ford Mondeo Diesel (93 - 96) L to N	3465
Ford Orion (83 - Sept 90) up to H	1009
Ford Sierra 4 cyl. (82 - 93) up to K	0903
Ford Sierra V6 (82 - 91) up to J	0904
Ford Transit Petrol (Mk 2) (78 - Jan 86) up to C	0719
Ford Transit Petrol (Mk 3) (Feb 86 - 89) C to G	1468
Ford Transit Diesel (Feb 86 - 99) C to T	3019
Ford 1.6 & 1.8 litre Diesel Engine (84 - 96) A to N	1172
Ford 2.1, 2.3 & 2.5 litre Diesel Engine (77 - 90) up to H	1606
FREIGHT ROVER	
Freight Rover Sherpa (74 - 87) up to E	0463
HILLMAN	
Hillman Avenger (70 - 82) up to Y	0037
HONDA	
Honda Accord (76 - Feb 84) up to A	0351
Honda Civic (Feb 84 - Oct 87) A to E	1226
Honda Civic (Nov 91 - 96) J to N	3199
HYUNDAI	
Hyundai Pony (85 - 94) C to M	3398
JAGUAR	
Jaguar E Type (61 - 72) up to L	0140
Jaguar MkI & II, 240 & 340 (55 - 69) up to H	0098
Jaguar XJ6, XJ & Sovereign; Daimler Sovereign (68 - Oct 86) up to D	0242
Jaguar XJ6 & Sovereign (Oct 86 - Sept 94) D to M	3261
Jaguar XJ12, XJS & Sovereign; Daimler Double Six (72 - 88) up to F	0478
JEEP	
Jeep Cherokee Petrol (93 - 96) K to N	1943
LADA	
Lada 1200, 1300, 1500 & 1600 (74 - 91) up to J	0413
Lada Samara (87 - 91) D to J	1610
LAND ROVER	
Land Rover 90, 110 & Defender Diesel (83 - 95) up to N	3017
Land Rover Discovery Diesel (89 - 95) G to N	3016
Land Rover Series IIA & III Diesel (58 - 85) up to C	0529
Land Rover Series II, IIA & III Petrol (58 - 85) up to C	0314
MAZDA	
Mazda 323 (Mar 81 - Oct 89) up to G	1608
Mazda 323 (Oct 89 - 98) G to R	3455
Mazda 626 (May 83 - Sept 87) up to E	0929
Mazda B-1600, B-1800 & B-2000 Pick-up (72 - 88) up to F	0267
MERCEDES BENZ	
Mercedes-Benz 190, 190E & 190D Petrol & Diesel (83 - 93) A to L	3450
Mercedes-Benz 200, 240, 300 Diesel (Oct 76 - 85) up to C	1114
Mercedes-Benz 250 & 280 (68 - 72) up to L	0346
Mercedes-Benz 250 & 280 (123 Series) (Oct 76 - 84) up to B	0677
Mercedes-Benz 124 Series (85 - Aug 93) C to K	3253
MG	
MGB (62 - 80) up to W	0111
MG Midget & AH Sprite (58 - 80) up to W	0265
MITSUBISHI	
Mitsubishi Shogun & L200 Pick-Ups (83 - 94) up to M	1944
MORRIS	
Morris Ital 1.3 (80 - 84) up to B	0705
Morris Minor 1000 (56 - 71) up to K	0024
NISSAN	
Nissan Bluebird (May 84 - Mar 86) A to C	1223
Nissan Bluebird (Mar 86 - 90) C to H	1473
Nissan Cherry (Sept 82 - 86) up to D	1031
Nissan Micra (83 - Jan 93) up to K	0931
Nissan Micra (93 - 99) K to T	3254
Nissan Primera (90 - Aug 99) H to T	1851
Nissan Stanza (82 - 86) up to D	0824
Nissan Sunny (May 82 - Oct 86) up to D	0895
Nissan Sunny (Oct 86 - Mar 91) D to H	1378
Nissan Sunny (Apr 91 - 95) H to N	3219
OPEL	
Opel Ascona & Manta (B Series) (Sept 75 - 88) up to F	0316
Opel Ascona (81 - 88) (Not available in UK see Vauxhall Cavalier 0812)	3215
Opel Astra (Oct 91 - Feb 98) (Not available in UK see Vauxhall Astra 1832)	3156
Opel Calibra (90 - 98) (See Vauxhall/Opel Calibra Book No. 3502)	
Opel Corsa (83 - Mar 93) (Not available in UK see Vauxhall Nova 0909)	3160
Opel Corsa (Mar 93 - 97) (Not available in UK see Vauxhall Corsa 1985)	3159
Opel Frontera Petrol & Diesel (91 - 98) (See Vauxhall/Opel Frontera Book No. 3454)	
Opel Kadett (Nov 79 - Oct 84)	0634
Opel Kadett (Oct 84 - Oct 91) (Not available in UK see Vauxhall Astra & Belmont 1136)	3196
Opel Omega & Senator (86 - 94) (Not available in UK see Vauxhall Carlton & Senator 1469)	3157
Opel Omega (94 - 99) (See Vauxhall/Opel Omega Book No. 3510)	
Opel Rekord (Feb 78 - Oct 86) up to D	0543

Title	Book No
Opel Vectra (Oct 88 - Oct 95) *(Not available in UK see Vauxhall Cavalier 1570)*	3158
Opel Vectra Petrol & Diesel (95 - 98) *(Not available in UK see Vauxhall Vectra 3396)*	3523

PEUGEOT

Title	Book No
Peugeot 106 Petrol & Diesel (91 - 98) J to S	1882
Peugeot 205 (83 - 95) A to N	0932
Peugeot 305 (78 - 89) up to G	0538
Peugeot 306 Petrol & Diesel (93 - 99) K to T	3073
Peugeot 309 (86 - 93) C to K	1266
Peugeot 405 Petrol (88 - 96) E to N	1559
Peugeot 405 Diesel (88 - 96) E to N	3198
Peugeot 406 Petrol & Diesel (96 - 97) N to R	3394
Peugeot 505 (79 - 89) up to G	0762
Peugeot 1.7/1.8 & 1.9 litre Diesel Engine (82 - 96) up to N	0950
Peugeot 2.0, 2.1, 2.3 & 2.5 litre Diesel Engines (74 - 90) up to H	1607

PORSCHE

Title	Book No
Porsche 911 (65 - 85) up to C	0264
Porsche 924 & 924 Turbo (76 - 85) up to C	0397

PROTON

Title	Book No
Proton (89 - 97) F to P	3255

RANGE ROVER

Title	Book No
Range Rover V8 (70 - Oct 92) up to K	0606

RELIANT

Title	Book No
Reliant Robin & Kitten (73 - 83) up to A	0436

RENAULT

Title	Book No
Renault 5 (Feb 85 - 96) B to N	1219
Renault 9 & 11 (82 - 89) up to F	0822
Renault 18 (79 - 86) up to D	0598
Renault 19 Petrol (89 - 94) F to M	1646
Renault 19 Diesel (89 - 95) F to N	1946
Renault 21 (86 - 94) C to M	1397
Renault 25 (84 - 92) B to K	1228
Renault Clio Petrol (91 - May 98) H to R	1853
Renault Clio Diesel (91 - June 96) H to N	3031
Renault Espace Petrol & Diesel (85 - 96) C to N	3197
Renault Fuego (80 - 86) up to C	0764
Renault Laguna Petrol & Diesel (94 - 96) L to P	3252
Renault Mégane & Scénic Petrol & Diesel (96 - 98) N to R	3395

ROVER

Title	Book No
Rover 213 & 216 (84 - 89) A to G	1116
Rover 214 & 414 (89 - 96) G to N	1689
Rover 216 & 416 (89 - 96) G to N	1830
Rover 211, 214, 216, 218 & 220 Petrol & Diesel (Dec 95 - 98) N to R	3399
Rover 414, 416 & 420 Petrol & Diesel (May 95 - 98) M to R	3453
Rover 618, 620 & 623 (93 - 97) K to P	3257
Rover 820, 825 & 827 (86 - 95) D to N	1380
Rover 3500 (76 - 87) up to E	0365
Rover Metro, 111 & 114 (May 90 - 96) G to N	1711

SAAB

Title	Book No
Saab 90, 99 & 900 (79 - Oct 93) up to L	0765
Saab 900 (Oct 93 - 98) L to R	3512
Saab 9000 (4-cyl) (85 - 95) C to N	1686

SEAT

Title	Book No
Seat Ibiza & Cordoba Petrol & Diesel (Oct 93 - Oct 99) L to V	3571
Seat Ibiza & Malaga (85 - 92) B to K	1609

SKODA

Title	Book No
Skoda Estelle (77 - 89) up to G	0604
Skoda Favorit (89 - 96) F to N	1801
Skoda Felicia Petrol & Diesel (95 - 99) M to T	3505

SUBARU

Title	Book No
Subaru 1600 & 1800 (Nov 79 - 90) up to H	0995

SUZUKI

Title	Book No
Suzuki SJ Series, Samurai & Vitara (4-cyl) (82 - 97) up to P	1942
Suzuki Supercarry (86 - Oct 94) C to M	3015

TALBOT

Title	Book No
Talbot Alpine, Solara, Minx & Rapier (75 - 86) up to D	0337
Talbot Horizon (78 - 86) up to D	0473
Talbot Samba (82 - 86) up to D	0823

TOYOTA

Title	Book No
Toyota Carina E (May 92 - 97) J to P	3256
Toyota Corolla (Sept 83 - Sept 87) A to E	1024
Toyota Corolla (80 - 85) up to C	0683
Toyota Corolla (Sept 87 - Aug 92) E to K	1683
Toyota Corolla (Aug 92 - 97) K to P	3259
Toyota Hi-Ace & Hi-Lux (69 - Oct 83) up to A	0304

TRIUMPH

Title	Book No
Triumph Acclaim (81 - 84) up to B	0792
Triumph GT6 & Vitesse (62 - 74) up to N	0112
Triumph Spitfire (62 - 81) up to X	0113
Triumph Stag (70 - 78) up to T	0441
Triumph TR7 (75 - 82) up to Y	0322

VAUXHALL

Title	Book No
Vauxhall Astra (80 - Oct 84) up to B	0635
Vauxhall Astra & Belmont (Oct 84 - Oct 91) B to J	1136
Vauxhall Astra (Oct 91 - Feb 98) J to R	1832
Vauxhall/Opel Calibra (90 - 98) G to S	3502
Vauxhall Carlton (Oct 78 - Oct 86) up to D	0480
Vauxhall Carlton & Senator (Nov 86 - 94) D to L	1469
Vauxhall Cavalier 1600, 1900 & 2000 (75 - July 81) up to W	0315
Vauxhall Cavalier (81 - Oct 88) up to F	0812
Vauxhall Cavalier (Oct 88 - 95) F to N	1570
Vauxhall Chevette (75 - 84) up to B	0285
Vauxhall Corsa (Mar 93 - 97) K to R	1985
Vauxhall/Opel Frontera Petrol & Diesel (91 - Sept 98) J to S	3454
Vauxhall Nova (83 - 93) up to K	0909
Vauxhall/Opel Omega (94 - 99) L to T	3510
Vauxhall Vectra Petrol & Diesel (95 - 98) N to R	3396
Vauxhall/Opel 1.5, 1.6 & 1.7 litre Diesel Engine (82 - 96) up to N	1222

VOLKSWAGEN

Title	Book No
Volkswagen Beetle 1200 (54 - 77) up to S	0036
Volkswagen Beetle 1300 & 1500 (65 - 75) up to P	0039
Volkswagen Beetle 1302 & 1302S (70 - 72) up to L	0110
Volkswagen Beetle 1303, 1303S & GT (72 - 75) up to P	0159
Volkswagen Golf & Jetta Mk 1 1.1 & 1.3 (74 - 84) up to A	0716
Volkswagen Golf, Jetta & Scirocco Mk 1 1.5,1.6 & 1.8 (74 - 84) up to A	0726
Volkswagen Golf & Jetta Mk 1 Diesel (78 - 84) up to A	0451
Volkswagen Golf & Jetta Mk 2 (Mar 84 - Feb 92) A to J	1081
Volkswagen Golf & Vento Petrol & Diesel (Feb 92 - 96) J to N	3097
Volkswagen LT vans & light trucks (76 - 87) up to E	0637
Volkswagen Passat & Santana (Sept 81 - May 88) up to E	0814
Volkswagen Passat Petrol & Diesel (May 88 - 96) E to P	3498
Volkswagen Polo & Derby (76 - Jan 82) up to X	0335
Volkswagen Polo (82 - Oct 90) up to H	0813
Volkswagen Polo (Nov 90 - Aug 94) H to L	3245
Volkswagen Polo Hatchback Petrol & Diesel (94 - 99) M to S	3500
Volkswagen Scirocco (82 - 90) up to H	1224
Volkswagen Transporter 1600 (68 - 79) up to V	0082
Volkswagen Transporter 1700, 1800 & 2000 (72 - 79) up to V	0226
Volkswagen Transporter (air-cooled) (79 - 82) up to Y	0638
Volkswagen Transporter (water-cooled) (82 - 90) up to H	3452

VOLVO

Title	Book No
Volvo 142, 144 & 145 (66 - 74) up to N	0129
Volvo 240 Series (74 - 93) up to K	0270
Volvo 262, 264 & 260/265 (75 - 85) up to C	0400
Volvo 340, 343, 345 & 360 (76 - 91) up to J	0715
Volvo 440, 460 & 480 (87 - 97) D to P	1691
Volvo 740 & 760 (82 - 91) up to J	1258
Volvo 850 (92 - 96) J to P	3260
Volvo 940 (90 - 96) H to N	3249
Volvo S40 & V40 (96 - 99) N to V	3569
Volvo S70, V70 & C70 (96 - 99) P to V	3573

YUGO/ZASTAVA

Title	Book No
Yugo/Zastava (81 - 90) up to H	1453

AUTOMOTIVE TECHBOOKS

Title	Book No
Automotive Brake Manual	3050
Automotive Carburettor Manual	3288
Automotive Diagnostic Fault Codes Manual	3472
Automotive Diesel Engine Service Guide	3286
Automotive Disc Brake Manual	3542
Automotive Electrical and Electronic Systems Manual	3049
Automotive Engine Management and Fuel Injection Systems Manual	3344
Automotive Gearbox Overhaul Manual	3473
Automotive Service Summaries Manual	3475
Automotive Timing Belts Manual – Austin/Rover	3549
Automotive Timing Belts Manual - Ford	3474
Automotive Timing Belts Manual – Peugeot/Citroën	3568
Automotive Timing Belts Manual – Vauxhall/Opel	3577
Automotive Welding Manual	3053
In-Car Entertainment Manual (3rd Edition)	3363

OTHER TITLES

Title	Book No
Haynes Diesel Engine Systems & Data Book (91 -00)	3548
Haynes Petrol Models Data Book (94 - 00)	3718

CL09.04/00

Preserving Our Motoring Heritage

< The Model J Duesenberg Derham Tourster. Only eight of these magnificent cars were ever built – this is the only example to be found outside the United States of America

Almost every car you've ever loved, loathed or desired is gathered under one roof at the Haynes Motor Museum. Over 300 immaculately presented cars and motorbikes represent every aspect of our motoring heritage, from elegant reminders of bygone days, such as the superb Model J Duesenberg to curiosities like the bug-eyed BMW Isetta. There are also many old friends and flames. Perhaps you remember the 1959 Ford Popular that you did your courting in? The magnificent 'Red Collection' is a spectacle of classic sports cars including AC, Alfa Romeo, Austin Healey, Ferrari, Lamborghini, Maserati, MG, Riley, Porsche and Triumph.

A Perfect Day Out

Each and every vehicle at the Haynes Motor Museum has played its part in the history and culture of Motoring. Today, they make a wonderful spectacle and a great day out for all the family. Bring the kids, bring Mum and Dad, but above all bring your camera to capture those golden memories for ever. You will also find an impressive array of motoring memorabilia, a comfortable 70 seat video cinema and one of the most extensive transport book shops in Britain. The Pit Stop Cafe serves everything from a cup of tea to wholesome, home-made meals or, if you prefer, you can enjoy the large picnic area nestled in the beautiful rural surroundings of Somerset.

> John Haynes O.B.E., Founder and Chairman of the museum at the wheel of a Haynes Light 12.

< Graham Hill's Lola Cosworth Formula 1 car next to a 1934 Riley Sports.

The Museum is situated on the A359 Yeovil to Frome road at Sparkford, just off the A303 in Somerset. It is about 40 miles south of Bristol, and 25 minutes drive from the M5 intersection at Taunton.
Open 9.30am - 5.30pm (10.00am - 4.00pm Winter) 7 days a week, *except Christmas Day, Boxing Day and New Years Day*
Special rates available for schools, coach parties and outings Charitable Trust No. 292048